A HOLE IN MY LIFE
BATTLING CHRONIC DIZZINESS

PHILIPPA THOMSON

Dedicated to Georgie

CONTENTS

AUTHOR'S NOTE

He who has health, has hope;
and he who has hope, has everything.

THOMAS CARLYLE, SCOTTISH PHILOSOPHER

This book is primarily about a relatively rare inner ear disorder, and how it has affected my life, but the scope is actually much broader than that. I set out to write the book that I wished had been available when I needed it myself. It is aimed at everyone who may experience dizziness, in all its manifestations, and who needs a better understanding of what might be happening to them. It is also for those treating, or caring for, anxious and/ or dizzy people.

I was faced with a series of complicated medical challenges. I have chosen not to water down, or eliminate, any of the detailed information I acquired as a result of that, but to reveal it in the most accessible way possible, within a narrative. A book needs to stimulate and entertain, but I hope this one will educate as well, and raise awareness of all ear and balance disorders.

I have been privileged to have unlimited access to the learning of one of the world's leading experts in this field, Dr Gerard Gianoli, and I have taken full advantage of that. It's hard to think of a question I haven't asked him, and had answered. I have furthermore undertaken an extensive amount of research myself, during my long quest to get well, as well as in the process of writing the book. Dr Gianoli and his partner, Dr James Soileau, have both read the entire contents of the book, and given their approval, so readers can rest assured that the medical information is accurate.

This is a true story, with my recollection of events, and I have related them to the best of my knowledge. I have, however, changed some names and identifying details, to protect the privacy of those individuals. I do not seek to apportion blame to anyone, but there are lessons that can be learned from my experiences.

A HOLE IN MY LIFE

1

SPEECHLESS

It could have been my shining moment. But it wasn't.

'Come on out now missy, stop hiding in there,' said Andrew. 'Everyone is gathering and we're waiting for you. I told them five o'clock, and it's just a couple of minutes before that now.'

I was hovering around my desk, pretending to sort through papers ready for my departure the next day. It was December 1999, I was alone in the open plan office I shared with editorial colleagues at Phaidon Press in London, and my new millennium was about to start afresh, all the way up in Scotland, in a pretty seaside town close to Edinburgh.

I looked up at him, frowning, and pulled a face.

'Oh, I wish you hadn't done that. I asked you not to,' I said. He beamed at me, and let out one of his hearty guffaws.

I had every reason to think my boss of nearly ten years had lined up some complimentary tales to tell in his valedictory speech, but I'd been dreading this moment since the previous day when he hinted what was in store. My hands were now clammy, and a furry lining had developed inside my dry mouth, as I contemplated the prospect of standing out on a limb in front of the assembled staff, while the speech unfolded. All eyes would be on me. My heart began thumping, and the few swigs of vodka that I'd imbibed just before Andrew's head popped around my door weren't providing the calming effect, or courage boost, that I needed. They were more likely contributing to the feeling of nausea slowly sidling in. The alcohol – just a small dose from an unlabelled, plastic bottle hiding in my bag, taken neat for convenience's sake – had become an increasingly relied-upon prop in recent years, whenever I was confronted with a social situation that I suspected would be my undoing.

I followed him out into the large open area, a vast expanse of clear glass at the far end, overlooking Regent's Canal, now transformed into a sombre, black curtain. People were milling around chatting to one another, and the sounds were rippling around the cavernous, double storey foyer of the converted wharf building. Andrew began talking, and I stared down at one of the shiny buckles on my suede shoes, trying to focus on it, and stop the swaying feeling that was starting to build up. I knew I needed all my concentration just to remain standing there, upright and steady, but I also had to try to take in some of the words so that I could smile, albeit in a forced manner, at the right moments. And there were plenty of them, as he spent a good ten minutes rattling through my employment history, alluding to a marriage and two children that had occurred within the same time frame, and rounding things off with some warm praise for all my efforts in clearing picture rights and coordinating research on *Century* – the company's enormous photographic record of the century about to end. I had a right to feel proud.

A sea of expectant faces now turned to stare at me, eager to hear what I had to say in response to the generous summary. It was one of those ghastly occasions, and I'd been experiencing more and more of them as the months rolled by, when I knew exactly what was expected of me, but I simply couldn't deliver. I steadied myself, trying to block out the pumping heart and the swimming head. I managed to force out several words, hopelessly insufficient ones.

'Thank you very much, Andrew.'

Then, shuffling round stiffly in the direction of my crowd, 'I begged him not to do this but, as you'll all appreciate, he hates to be told no.' The awkward announcement made it sound as though the managing director had been forcing his unwanted attentions on me.

'I've been here a long time, and I shall miss you all very much. I hope some of you will come along for a drink after work tomorrow.'

And that was it. The expectant faces changed to puzzled, disappointed ones. Hardly surprising, as I discovered minutes later, when I unwrapped my presents, that my friends and colleagues had been contributing to a very expensive Georg Jensen silver bangle and an enormous bouquet of flowers. My paltry few words didn't seem a fair return.

It hadn't just been a case of minor stage fright. I had managed, thankfully, to stave off a full blown panic attack, but I left for home that evening feeling dejected and bemused. Why did this keep happening to me, and how was I going to get it under control? Was I just under too much stress from a pressurised job and the care of a severely disabled three-year-old son, and would everything start to improve in my new, family-orientated life in the north? If only I'd known that, thousands of miles away in Baltimore, an American had already come up with the answers.

2

PRESSURE DROP

When I learned that epilepsy would be a permanent fixture in my child's life, a fierce protective instinct kicked in and, close behind it, a state of constant fear and worry for the one I loved. Once I had taken in that the eight-month-old baby would never grow up to do the things my firstborn would be able to do, I entered a very slow and protracted period of grieving. It wasn't a grief I was able to share with anyone. If that sounds a little detached, it's because even now, years later, words don't come easily to explain the extreme sense of loss that I experienced, and kept secret.

In fact the grieving, for the lost child that could have been, never goes away, it just retreats. The clinical psychologist Simone Korff-Sausse has commented that new parents of disabled children suffer from the lack of symbolisation that is necessary for mourning. As they aren't able to put something in place of the 'lost' object, their grief reoccurs, like trauma, with great intensity at key points in the person's life; the process of mourning is never complete. Every miniscule sign of progress did, however, bring with it some small comfort and a sense of achievement. Patrick's chromosome disorder, as it turned out, was so rare that when it was eventually diagnosed, over three years after our move to Scotland when he was six, even the charity Unique with its worldwide database described it as extremely unusual. No-one on their records came close to matching his particular rearrangement of chromosomes, with their mosaic pattern, and an apparent loss of genetic material when it had moved over from one chromosome to another – what is called a balanced translocation.

My husband and I had spent those first six years of Patrick's life trying every form of stimulation, encouragement, physical exercise and health supplement that we could lay our hands on, in an effort to get our dimpled, blue-eyed boy, with his mop of blond curls, up on his feet, putting one in front of the other. As no-one could tell us what was actually wrong, despite a round of clinical tests while under hospital observation, we'd taken him on a long journey to Somerset, to be assessed at Brainwave for a home-based programme of exercises. We carried them out religiously, at the start of each morning, for months and months. We spent a week at a time near the Listening Centre in Sussex so that he could spend two hours a day engulfed in a pair of large headphones, receiving sensori-neural integration input. And a series of regular cranial osteopathy sessions, both in London and Edinburgh, were slotted in.

When the genetic specialist at the Western General Hospital, in Edinburgh, took a look at Patrick's rather distinctive arrangement of facial features, and watched him tottering a few yards along a corridor with his wide gait, he requested permission to examine him more closely. On finding some very faint pigmentation swirls around his abdomen, he declared with confidence, 'I think we can get to the bottom of this.'

Along with the tears, a relief of sorts accompanied the diagnosis weeks later, when the elaborate laboratory tests on a skin biopsy were complete. At long last I could set aside the nagging doubts: Should I have done something differently throughout the pregnancy? Had a terrible medical mishap occurred during the delivery? It transpired to be just a case of chronic bad luck, cells misbehaving at the time of conception. We were informed that the disorder wasn't an inherited one, and therefore wouldn't affect his sister. It was a relief simply to know what we were dealing with. It was now time to try and get on with the daily task of maximising Patrick's potential, and get back to living, as Dolly Parton would have told us.

Relocation to Scotland was the result of a number of factors coming together at the same time. With two children under six, a congested capital no longer held the same attraction, and we had begun investigating rural areas within commuting distance, but with little enthusiasm for the travelling involved. Juggling my demanding job of managing tight picture budgets and book deadlines three days a week, with the endless round of appointments for my son in the remaining two, was becoming increasingly hard, and neither task was getting my undivided attention. The Scottish Parliament opened for business in 1999, and opened up new job opportunities in Edinburgh so, after much discussion between us, my husband decided to take one of them up.

It also offered me the chance to escape. From the friends and neighbours who, considerately trying to find appropriate vocabulary, would refer to Patrick as 'special', when in fact the honesty of 'disabled' might have been more helpful in moving our lives forward. And from the local baby and then toddler groups, where it was all too apparent my baby and then toddler wasn't reaching the milestones he was supposed to. Far from it, as he stayed firmly put at the baby stage. As far as I was concerned, it would be a fresh start for all of us, and I could focus on my family, even though I had never anticipated being a full-time, stay-at-home mother. I loved my picture research work, tracking down and acquiring images for beautifully produced art and design books, but something had to give. There was a downside of course, there usually is – we would be a long way away from our respective families. My paternal grandmother had grown up across the water in Fife, so I chose to look at it as a chance to reconnect with my Scottish roots.

One of the advantages of having a primary school-age child was the ease with which I could meet other mothers in the playground, at the beginning or end of the school day. Switching from a fast-paced city life to the picturesque but rather quaint seaside town of North Berwick took some adjusting to, and my English accent, townie appearance, plus a little boy emitting alien roaring noises from his pushchair, made it somewhat difficult to blend into my surroundings, always my preferred option. Early on I struck up conversation with Christine, a bright-eyed, diminutive nurse, mother of three, who suggested we get together for coffee. She had also moved up from England several years earlier, and so there was plenty of common ground. Her youngest was, like my daughter, in Primary 2, and Christine later introduced me to a couple of others with daughters the same age. We became firm friends, and it wasn't long before we came up with the idea of leaving our children with their fathers, for a weekend away.

And so it transpired that, in May 2003, the four of us, in our forties, were sitting on an aeroplane at Edinburgh airport, ready for take-off to Amsterdam. We were all looking forward to a break from our home routines, but I was especially. My pre-Patrick life now well behind me, I was immersed in a world of therapists, social workers, paediatricians and epilepsy clinics, and it was hard not to feel daunted by the thought that this was how things would be from now on. It wasn't the motherhood I had bargained for, but changing and adapting wasn't an option either. I had to, and life had to. I was now the main carer for a small person who was totally dependent on me, for whom absolutely everything had to be done, and I was determined to rise to the challenge. I had forged a tight bond with my little man from the very moment he emerged into the world. Always on the alert now for the throaty sound of expulsion of air at the start of a fit, deep sleep was a thing of the past. The prospect of two uninterrupted nights was something to get seriously excited about – I could completely switch off from my parenting duties, and relax for a whole weekend. It was somewhat annoying that I had managed to do something silly the day before leaving. Half an hour of garden clearing had left me with a broken rose thorn deeply imbedded down the side of my finger, and it resisted all my attempts to extract it.

'Let's hope the hotel's as nice as the one in Dublin. Was the trip in May last year, or later?' I asked Christine.

Dublin had been our first experimental long weekend away, and had been such a resounding success that we decided to repeat it in another city. I had taken charge of booking the accommodation this time.

'The rooms looked attractive on the website, and it seems to be in a good location for sight seeing,' I said. 'Are we going to go to the Van Gogh Museum tomorrow morning? It's just over the road from the hotel.'

I was sitting next to Christine, and we flipped through our guidebooks discussing what we'd like to fit in during the short stay. We had a laugh about some of our Dublin memories, and then talked about what should be done with my finger once we got to the hotel room we were sharing, as it was throbbing now and starting to swell up. It was obviously infected. To add to my discomfort, I also had the congested early signs of a cold setting in. Neither of us were nervous flyers, but some of the passengers near us looked distinctly on edge during the turbulent ride. The seatbelts must remain fastened light seemed to be on more than off. It was when the descent into Schiphol airport began that those expressions became more panic-stricken, particularly when the plane lurched downwards with a very sudden drop in pressure.

'Oww! Ouch, that really hurt. Did you feel that Christine?'

I was cupping my left ear protectively, as it seemed as though someone had just pierced a dagger deep down inside it. It was a brutally sharp pain. Christine grimaced.

'Yes, my ears hurt then. I hope the pilot knows what he's doing. What if it's the first time he's landed a plane?' she replied.

He did seem to know, as we hit the ground safely not long afterwards.

Once we had reconvened with our companions Cathy and Maureen, we exchanged symptoms and found that, to varying degrees, we all had the uncomfortable blocked sensation, and a desire to keep un-popping ears that refused to un-pop. My sharp pain had subsided and a muffledness taken its place but, as I now had a pulsating, pink sausage finger, that took precedence. The Van Gogh Museum, the world's largest trove with some 200 paintings and 500 drawings by the virtuoso, was bustling the next morning, in the 150th year of the artist's birthday. Out of the four of us, I was the only one with a modicum of art history knowledge but, even with the finger now doused in antiseptic and securely swaddled, the effort of contributing snippets of information about the works on show soon proved too much for my cotton wool stuffed head. The all too familiar disequilibrium was starting to take hold, as we weaved our way through the crowd. I held onto Cathy's arm.

'I hope you don't mind if I cling onto you?' I said. 'That flight has made me go a bit deaf, and it's affecting my balance in here, with the noise of all the people moving around.'

This was only partially true. I had first become fully aware of the hostile effects of art galleries eleven years previously. It was 1992 and, as picture editor at the art book publisher Phaidon Press, my presence was expected at the book launch party for the Portuguese painter Paula Rego at Marlborough Fine Art, one of the commercial galleries that inhabit Albemarle Street, in the exclusive quarter of Mayfair. With a resolute new owner Richard Schlagman in his signature Armani suit at the helm, and a graphic design guru Alan Fletcher steering the course, the small publishing company was slowly but surely turning things around, from its near financial collapse a couple of years back. It was a balmy evening, and fashionable Londoners were soon filling up the airy space on its stripped wooden floors, the theatre actress Harriet Walter and the musician, and up and coming television presenter, Jools Holland among them. Marlborough was known for its representation of cutting edge contemporary artists, and Rego's work was currently on exhibition.

My role was to mingle with the invited guests, stimulate an interest in the book which was on display for potential buyers, and maintain a charming and relaxed demeanour as one of the representatives of the new-look Phaidon Press. Not being the most gregarious of personalities, this wasn't my favourite way to pass the time, but a bashful smile from Richard across the room seemed to indicate that my cream jacket and navy, polka dot dress combination had met with his approval, and I steeled myself to give the event my best shot. However, I very quickly felt out of my depth. The gallery had rapidly turned into a babbling, shimmering swirl of painted faces and clinking wine glasses, and I started to overheat. I took several deep breaths while lurking around the open entrance door, and then willed myself back into the throng. I could feel the panic steadily working its way up my body, as I aimlessly manoeuvred around the room, studiously avoiding meeting anyone's gaze in case they tried to talk to me.

I felt a tap on my shoulder, and slowly swivelled round. Every move had to be made slowly.

'Philippa. Hello. Oh, you work for Phaidon now, do you?' she said, zooming in on the name badge pinned to my lapel.

I'd known Melissa, only vaguely, several years before, and as she was now cradling a sleepy toddler in her arms, it was clear she wanted to share her happy change in circumstances with me.

'This is Jack, we're not staying long. It's nearly his bedtime. A lot has happened since I last saw you.'

Her words drifted away into the buzzing hubbub around us, and I looked at her vacantly, with a fixed smile on my face, wondering whether she'd noticed my gentle swaying, and put it down to a glass too many. As soon as I sensed an opportunity, I mumbled a few words about being needed elsewhere, and slipped into a small adjoining room where several staff had congregated.

'Is anyone using this chair?' I whispered feebly. 'I'm feeling quite sick, and need to sit down. I think I must be going down with some sort of bug.'

A willowy marketing assistant broke off her conversation to tell me I looked rather pale, and she went to fetch a glass of water. My hand was shaking as I raised it to my lips for a sip. I spent most of the next hour hiding in my corner, venturing out briefly now and again as the gallery space started to empty out, just to show my face. The unhappy episode gave my confidence a battering. A charming and relaxed demeanour had most definitely not been maintained. Book launches are part and parcel of the publishing world, and I already feared the next one.

. . .

Back out in the fresh air on Paulus Potterstraat, I felt steady enough to release Cathy's arm, and I could finally hear more normally again. The rest of the weekend passed quickly with no major incident, apart from very nearly missing the return flight because of an excess of chat, coffee, and crepes in the airport lounge. My finger wasn't improving though, and I very quickly arranged a visit to a local GP for a course of antibiotics. I mentioned the stuffed up feeling in my left ear, explaining what had caused it.

'Hold your nose, and blow out with your mouth closed,' he replied, 'as though you were blowing up a balloon. It's called a Valsalva manoeuvre. That should clear things up if you keep doing it regularly, every so often.'

And that's what I did, but it didn't. At the next visit to the same GP many weeks later, after a cursory glance inside the troubled ear, a decongestant was proposed.

'Squirt one or two sprays in each nostril. That should clear things up if you keep doing it regularly, every so often.' I wasn't entirely convinced.

There wasn't any pain, and I didn't have spare time for non-essential medical appointments, but by June the proceeding year things had accelerated to the 'I've really had enough of this' stage. Having established that the wait for a routine ENT consultation on the National Health Service might be as much as six months, I booked myself a private appointment in Edinburgh, courtesy of a limited health insurance package that I was entitled to through my spouse's employer. I felt positively wicked, never before having paid to see a private doctor, and being an avid supporter of the country's highly valued NHS. In choosing an appropriate doctor, I first had to get to grips with the terminology. Doctors at the senior level were referred to as consultants. Those who were consultant surgeons could, if they chose, adopt the title Mr, rather than Dr. It was a form of inverted snobbery that dated back to the Middle Ages, when surgeons served an apprenticeship like other tradesmen, whereas physicians completed a university degree.

Mr Sanderson (doctor no.1) motioned to me to enter the room. S for smug, I quickly determined. His manner was brusque without actually overstepping the boundaries of politeness, and he clearly had no interest in the story of my flying experience, which I started to tell. A swift examination of both ears was undertaken, followed by a hearing test, with me still ensconced in the same chair, not in a separate booth as I'd imagined. Nothing seemed very thorough about his approach.

'You have quite a noticeable high tone, sensorineural hearing loss on the right side. Are you aware of that?'

My first thought was, 'what on earth is sensorineural hearing?' (but I had no intention of letting on to Mr Smug); my second thought, 'I've come to have my left ear looked at, and he's telling me something is wrong with the right one'; and my third thought, 'this isn't the first time someone's mentioned hearing loss to me.'

It had been at the Listening Centre, during Patrick's initial visit, two years ago. Dr Tomatis, a French ear, nose and throat specialist, was one of the pioneers in the field of sound and music therapy, and his dedicated work brought new insights to the role of the ear in human development. By training the ear to listen better, he believed it was possible to improve its functioning, and he applied his discoveries to people with all sorts of learning disabilities, as well as many others who encountered speech or singing problems. Alex Smith, a bearded, softly-spoken Scotsman, had spent time learning the techniques with Dr Tomatis in Paris, as he had seen firsthand the rewards accrued for his son Luke. He set up the complex equipment in a cramped, old studio in Lewes, a short distance from the south coast of England, and my whole family trekked down there from our new Scottish home, hundreds of miles north. As Patrick was unable to speak, and couldn't therefore complete a meaningful hearing test at the outset, Alex offered me one instead.

At the end of it, he looked at me askance, and said: 'Can you think of any reason why you might have a sudden falling off in your hearing in the right ear? The left one is normal. It's nothing to get worried about, you can obviously hear alright, but it is unusual.'

I was taken aback. I hadn't expected Alex to find anything wrong at all with my hearing, and I'd only agreed to the test as it seemed churlish not to.

'No, I haven't a clue. I didn't know I had any sort of hearing problem,' I replied.

Alex probed a bit more.

'Have you ever worked in a particularly noisy environment, or used any sort of loud machinery?'

He drew a blank.

'I can only think it was all those rock concerts I went to in my younger days,' I said, smiling.

I brushed it off, and thought nothing more of it, up until Mr Sanderson's finding.

The consultant now reached over his desk to push an index card into my hand, on which he had scribbled MRI scan, but the only explanation given was that it would be advisable to investigate the loss of hearing. When I asked about the left side, the side he was supposed to be diagnosing for the costly twenty-minute, one-sided conversation, he shrugged his shoulders and said it looked fine. Shaking my hand, he added that a letter would go to my GP, and then ushered me out of his consulting room. It wasn't an auspicious start to my engagement with private health care.

Of course, once I was home, I looked up sensorineural, and it dawned on me that that hearing was gone for good. Once the tiny cochlear hair cells are damaged, it's irreversible. I'd gone hoping to sort out one problem, and returned with a completely new one.

3

A SUSTAINED CACOPHONY OF NOISE

'What scan appointment?'

The doctors' receptionist couldn't find a record of any such request, when I chased up the consultant's referral six months later. I had delayed for that length of time as I'd been warned non-urgent investigations involved a considerable wait, but when I discovered that I hadn't even been waiting, my patience started to wane. One of the GPs, taking some responsibility for the oversight, hastily arranged a new ENT appointment, an NHS one this time. Early in 2005 I drove to the hospital to meet Mr Wood (doctor no.2) – W for well meaning, so it seemed on our first encounter.

The young, smartly turned-out doctor was newly appointed to his consultancy role, and he brimmed with energy, positivity and pleasantness.

'Please take a seat,' he said. 'Let's start at the beginning, and you tell me everything that's happened so far. Then I'll do a quick examination, and we'll decide where to go from there.'

My summary complete, and nothing gleaned from an inspection of my ears, Mr Wood started making notes, wielding his fat, Montblanc fountain pen like a wand of authority.

'I understand there's been some sort of mix-up with a scan that was supposed to happen, so I'm putting you down for an urgent one this time. I can't say exactly when it'll be, but I'll see you again once the results are through. I'm sure we can find out what the problem is. Does that sound ok?'

I left feeling reassured. I was now in the hands of a competent doctor that wanted to help me.

Several more months passed without news, despite the supposed urgency. They were months filled increasingly with worry, as I knew the pressure sensation in my head was worsening, and having more and more of an impact on my day-to-day life. At the start of that year I had decided I wanted to get back into some sort of paid work, as I wasn't cut out for only a home-keeping role. Taking on bits of freelance picture research from my London contacts wasn't proving very fruitful, as the work was frequently offered when I wasn't available during the school holidays. There was minimal give and take in the marital division of responsibilities, a situation that had been weighing on my mind for a while, but I already had enough on my plate without starting to rock that particular boat. I decided to teach myself some basic desk-top publishing skills, and launch a free local business directory for which I could dictate the schedule, and take a small income from the advertising fees. Sinister headaches threatened to sabotage my efforts. I'd heard friends in the past describe debilitating migraines that would force them to take to their bed for hours in a blacked out room, and I had listened with sympathy, without fully comprehending their plight. I now found myself regularly laid low with a crushing headache that would wrap itself around my entire skull like an ill-fitting helmet and then, little by little, start tightening the screws.

This development was my secret so long as I could retire under the bedclothes when the pain reached an unacceptable level, but it gradually spilled over into times of the day when family members expected my input. Of course, when Patrick was home from his special needs school that was *all* the time, and my daughter Amy, being only eleven, needed her mother as well. It was time to prepare my husband for my acoustic neuroma diagnosis, as I was now convinced that the scan would reveal one. It had occurred to me that neither consultant had offered a satisfactory explanation for the need for an MRI. Out of my innumerable online searches I settled on this specific slow-growing tumour in the brain, one which affected the hearing, and for which severe headaches were a classic symptom, along with blurred vision. Yes, I was pretty sure my vision was blurred sometimes. It was a benign growth, but that was almost beside the point – a tumour could never be a good thing could it, and its removal must surely be dangerous? Google said it didn't grow quickly, so I could only hope that that would be in my favour, and the interminable delays in getting the scan wouldn't have cost valuable time.

By August 2005, the month of the scan, it would be fair to say I was a nervous wreck. When it comes to being encased inside a narrow tunnel for half an hour, forbidden from twitching a muscle, with excruciatingly loud thudding, clanking and banging noises ricocheting around the tube, the status nervous wreck is not a recommended starting point. Having an MRI scan involves lying in a strong magnetic field with radio-frequency waves being directed at your body, and the hideous racket emanates from the rapid expansion and contraction of the large, metal coil containing the three smaller magnets.

As I reticently positioned myself flat on my back, the female radiographer said, 'I know you haven't had a scan like this before. It's very important that you keep absolutely still throughout the procedure, but you can press this buzzer if at any point you need us to stop. Obviously try not to use it, if you can help it – if the imaging process is interrupted, we may have to start all over again. I'd like you to put on these headphones please. We can talk to you through them, and also play you some music. What would you like to listen to?'

I had been forewarned about the claustrophobic nature of the experience, so music sounded like a welcome distraction.

'Some classical music would be nice, something soothing and relaxing please,' I replied.

She locked me into my capsule, the gentle Chopin prelude lulling me into a floating repose. A few encouraging words filtered through. And then the torture began. It built up gradually with some minor clanging and clattering, but progressed to a sustained cacophony of noise. Were they using a pneumatic drill? My body was rigid with tension, my hand ached from gripping the panic buzzer, and my head seemed to be pulsating. Staring out through the porthole at the radiographers in their control chamber only upped my anxiety level to bursting point. Closing my eyes to focus on the music hurtled me down into a spiral of dizziness. But tilting them up, wide open, to the roof of my prison unleashed a fog of nausea. There was no escaping the torment. I felt as though the vibrations would cause my disintegration at any minute. I had held off moving for what seemed like an eternity, but the urge to vomit now overwhelmed me. I pressed the buzzer, and gesticulated that urgent release was required.

The radiographer came rushing through, with a small cardboard basin in her hand. My ashen face had presumably made my intentions known. She sat me up on the moveable bed, and held out a glass of water.

'Take your time. You're by no means the first person this has happened to. Can I get you anything else?'

I shook my head, and took very deep breaths, trying to relax and think myself into a different place. After a short spell of respite she said, 'I'm afraid we really ought to carry on now, as there's another patient waiting. We've looked at the images, and fortunately we can just backtrack to the beginning of that sequence. It should only mean about a further ten minutes.'

I handed her the empty basin, and somehow propelled myself back into the chamber. Even in my anguished state I was fully aware that if I was ever going to get well, I first had to find out what was wrong. That's what I needed the scan to reveal.

The drive home gave me time for reflection. MRI scans now had to be added to my ever-growing list of panic attack triggers. Perhaps this one wasn't so surprising; the radiographer had told me after all that she'd seen a similar reaction many times before. But I still found the incident unsettling. It brought to mind a very different event, a friend's engagement party a long time ago when I was about twenty-four. We had arrived at the door of Caroline's small, terraced West London house rather later than invited, as my journalist boyfriend's copy deadline had held things up. Caroline, poured into her skintight leather jeans, cigarette in hand, was her usual ebullient self, and she greeted us warmly. We were steered into the tiny kitchen crammed full with strangers, and instructed to pour ourselves drinks. It was like trying to squeeze through a jam-packed underground train in the rush hour, only with shrill passengers not silent ones. Loud music was blaring out from the adjoining room where more guests were dancing. I was already in a fractious mood because of our tardiness but, within half an hour of being in the throbbing hothouse, my mental stamina ebbed away, and the ability to socially interact slipped out of reach. I had trouble keeping my glass of wine steady in my shaking hand, and the more I worried that people were looking at this, the more the anxiety escalated. I clutched onto the edge of my boyfriend's jacket while he mingled and chatted, until I insisted we make our excuses to Caroline and her fiancée. We had been the last to arrive, and the first to leave. Parties had been on the panic list for a considerable time.

·   ·   ·

Greeting Mr Wood for the second time, I sensed he was no longer the relaxed, confident doctor of our first meeting. I pondered whether that had resulted from eight stressful months as an NHS consultant.

Looking up from his paperwork he said, 'I'm sorry you had to wait longer than I expected for the scan. But you don't have MS.'

My mind flew into overdrive. I hadn't had an inkling anyone thought I might have multiple sclerosis.

'Of course I'm very glad to know that, but has the scan shown anything at all? I had assumed it would be looking for an acoustic neuroma.'

'No, nothing, it was clear,' he replied, confirming as well that such a growth had been a possibility.

To my amazement, he seemed to assume I would take this as my exit cue. I pushed myself into the seat of the chair, to indicate my resistance to that idea. The words came out in a stream.

'But something's very wrong. I've been getting much worse since I last saw you. I mentioned my headaches before, but now they're happening every day, and sometimes they're terrible. I can't function normally any more.'

My voice started to break.

'I feel dizzy a lot of the time, and the nausea is constant on some days. And the pressure in my ear just makes everything harder to cope with.'

He looked concerned. 'What about tinnitus?' he said. 'Do you ever have any?'

Tinnitus to me was loud ringing in the ears and I didn't have that on my list of symptoms, so I omitted to mention the other strange sounds that invaded my inner sanctum from time to time. The consultant admitted he was perplexed.

'I'm going to do a more detailed examination inside your nasal passages and the one to your ear, so I need to spray some anaesthetic to numb everything,' he said. 'I'd better warn you, you may get a slightly unpleasant taste at the back of your mouth.'

The taste wasn't too awful compared to the discomfort from the endoscopy. At the end of it we were no further forward.

Then the doctor produced a metal instrument which he called his tuning fork, and struck it against the bony edge of his palm so that the forked end vibrated gently. Before I had time to question what cruel deed he had in mind this time, he was placing it on various parts of my head and behind my ears, asking me to tell him what I could hear. He nodded and scribbled a few notes, but there was no discussion about his findings, and I was beginning to feel strangely excluded from the whole process. I needed to prevent Mr Well Meaning from morphing into Mr What the Hell, so I sat patiently waiting to see what he would come up with.

'I think we'll have to see how things go over the next few months, and I'll book you in for a grommet insertion. I'll be honest – I don't know what the problem is, so there's no guarantee a ventilation tube in the ear drum will make any difference but, if you agree, I think it's probably worth a try.'

More weeks and months dragged on, day by dragging day. I had been gulping down an expensive potpourri of high-dose vitamins and minerals to give my immune system a massive bolstering, just in case an allergy was the suspect, or even Ménières disease. However, the classic drop attacks related to that inner ear condition, often lasting hours and sometimes accompanied by vomiting, were not plaguing me fortunately, so I eventually stopped the supplements, surmising that they may in fact be feeding the headaches.

My attempts to find an answer were becoming more desperate. A chiropractor was given the chance to offer her insight, but after examining my x-rays she declined to carry out any manipulations, failing to see any reason to. I was thankful for her honesty. My dentist was happy to consider that my uneven bite might have an adverse affect on the ear by way of TMJ – short for temporomandibular joint, or jawbone socket, disorder. For several months my night-time getup bore more than a passing resemblance to a rugby player's, while I persisted with a specially made mouth guard, and then added daily stretching exercises for tongue, teeth, jaw, neck (you name it, I stretched it), all to no avail. Whenever I could find the time, I treated myself to a shiatsu massage and at last found relief in the therapist's relaxing, rhythmic finger pressures. At the end of each visit she would comment on the accumulation of tension around my neck, and the tightness in my shoulders. We both assumed the physical strain of manoeuvring a growing young man, who had very limited mobility, must be the predominant cause, but there had been a vague hope that muscular imbalances could be contributing to the clogged ear.

Then of course there was the Chinese herb Jia-Wei-Gui-Pi-Tang, which I tracked down to a supplier in New York, and boiled to make a revolting cup of tea several times a day, but when my daughter caught me blowing up a balloon with my nose, then letting the air blow back in, I realised I might be starting to lose the plot. It still didn't stop me spending quite a large sum of money on a sophisticated version of this trick, a medical device called the EarPopper, which also had to be sourced in America.

It was now March 2006, and I was on the ward at eight am sharp, waiting to be admitted for my grommet day surgery. I had driven the fifty-five miles to the hospital on my own, and Hugh was collecting me in the afternoon as I wasn't allowed to drive myself home. I was second on the morning list, but was unexpectedly moved up to the number one slot. The striped curtain was whisked around the bed next to mine, and the anaesthetist talked in low tones with his elderly patient about what would happen to her. His voice suddenly rose.

'Excuse me, Mrs Dalgleish. Did you just say you had a cup of tea with milk before coming here? You aren't allowed to take anything, and certainly not milk, before a general anaesthetic. It is written down in the letter you have here. We're going to have to reschedule you for the afternoon.'

Consequently I was wheeled straight down to the operating room with a big X next to my left ear, put there with a black marker pen by the surgeon, a man I'd never met before. Many years had passed since my wisdom teeth extraction, when I had discovered my buried fear of waking up while anaesthetised but, as I was wheeled along on the gurney with the bright lights emanating from the theatre ahead of me, the old sinking feeling began to resurface. My wristband with name and date of birth were read at various control points, and just before I was sedated, amidst the usual banter aimed at relaxing the patient, I was asked as the final check what procedure I was having that morning.

'I'm having a grommet put into my ear on the left side,' I said, 'where the X is marked.'

Alarmed eyes peered at me over the surgical masks. They were about to get to work on a cochlear implant for lost hearing, not a ventilation tube. It seems the message about Mrs Dalgleish's forbidden cup of tea hadn't made it that far.

I knew within hours of getting home that the tube in my ear wasn't the solution I longed for, and I don't think I ever thought it would be. I had always considered myself a resourceful and resilient person, but the laborious process of trying to find out what was wrong was wearing me down. In his book *When Doctors Become Patients*, Robert Klitzman hit the nail on the head: 'A person waiting is a person suffering. The doctor came to realise as never before the importance of minutes, hours and days. The difference between being a doctor and not being a doctor was the timing.'

One of the worst aspects was one I hadn't anticipated – the lack of support from a medical system that I'd always held in high regard, and had trusted I could count on. The cherished National Health System, with its entrenched fairness of free healthcare for all at the point of access, was failing to come to my rescue because my problem needed time and expertise to solve it. It had become clear to me that for those who had an illness that couldn't be quickly identified there was an invisible net through which to fall. In other words, 'you're on your own, mate'. Once it had got to the stage where I was hoping for anything to be diagnosed, no matter how life threatening, I knew I was at a desperate point. I would never have believed I could be envious of a cancer patient.

There was another stumbling block. I wasn't good at asking for help. I was quietly struggling, suffering on the inside, and (mostly) smiling on the outside. I had two young children, and it was vitally important to me that I held things together for them, as much as I could; I hated the fact that I was an increasingly irritable and exhausted mother. The strains of dealing with a moody daughter approaching her teenage years, combined with the round-the-clock feeding, washing, carrying and entertaining of an adult-size toddler, were significant challenges on their own, but now there was a serious health problem to contend with, and no-one coming forward to help find a diagnosis. Family were all miles away, and although a number of close friends, not least my Amsterdam trio, were solicitous in asking how things were going, I didn't let on the extent to which the lack of progress was affecting me.

Autophony is literally defined as hearing self. More broadly interpreted, it refers not just to hearing your own voice loudly, but also other internal noises such as heartbeat and joint movements. By the time our Scottish summer had got underway, I was certain that it had become one of my symptoms. This was a breakthrough, perhaps a major one. I sent an email to Dr Kujawski in Zurich, as I ascertained that he treated an unusual condition called Patulous Eustachian Tube (shortened to P.E.T), for which this symptom was a classic sign. I wanted to know how much his surgery would cost – a crazy plan was taking shape in my mind, to fly over to see him and end the misery, as if by magic. In the absence of any suggestions from two consultants and several GPs, I'd been forced to widen my search, and undertake a thorough investigation. This potential diagnosis was certainly the most promising, and the immediate response from Dr Kujawski was refreshing. Sending more information about P.E.T. and the surgical procedure to fix it, he confirmed that it was a physical disorder where the Eustachian tube, normally closed, instead stays intermittently open. The little tube, just three to four centimetres long in adults, is a narrow passage that connects the cavity of the middle ear with the back of the nose. Its primary job is to enable the equalization of pressure on each side of the eardrum. Now I just needed to get myself a diagnosis.

Buoyed by my exciting detective work, I fired off more correspondence, this time to Mr Wood.

'I have an appointment in your clinic on June 20,' I wrote. 'Please could you test to see whether I have Patulous Eustachian Tube. I seem to have all the symptoms, as far as I can tell.' I had concluded that this was a safer approach, rather than making the demand on the spot. Robert Klitzman put my thoughts neatly into words in his book. 'I know that the doctor feels good if I trust him. The fewer questions I ask, and the more he knows that I feel I'm safe in his hands, the happier he is and the more positively he'll relate to me. I want him to know he's a good guy.' I was learning all the time about the inexplicit, but crucial, doctor patient relationship. I chose not to mention my dealings with Mr Kujawski in the letter.

Mr Wood showed me into his office again, and I felt nervous as I produced from my bag some written instructions for a P.E.T. test. I had no idea how he would react. Curiosity seemed to be getting the better of him, so I launched in.

'If you don't have any objection, it says here that the doctor needs to listen in one ear with his stethoscope, while the patient counts to ten. Then the doctor should listen in the other ear, while the patient counts again. The important thing is whether you can hear any difference between the two.'

Perhaps just deciding this was more fun than run-of-the-mill consultations, he bounced off to fetch a stethoscope, and we played the game. And then we did it again, just to be safe.

'Well, yes, I *could* be convinced that there's a difference between the two sides. The problem is, though, I know very little about Patulous Eustachian Tube, so I'd need to think about referring you elsewhere. I've a vague recollection there's a fellow in Dundee who's particularly interested in it. Do you want to leave it with me, and we'll let you know?'

I was so relieved that things had gone smoothly, it wasn't until later that I realised I had failed to ask when or how this information would be relayed. As it transpired, weeks passed and no information came, so this time I emailed the person who appeared to be the world's P.E.T. expert – Dr Dennis Poe, in Boston.

'I used to have a short period in the morning when the pressure wasn't too bad, but now it seems to be ever present, troubling me as soon as I wake,' I wrote. 'If I put my head between my knees, it can sometimes help, but not always. I have popping and crackling sounds in my ears and jaw, and I can hear my heart pounding up in my ear; so if I'm stressed or I've been running and am out of breath, there's a terrible, loud thumping noise. I hear my own voice echoing around my head when I speak – it's awful when I have to raise my voice to tell my daughter off, as it really hurts my head.'

What I particularly needed to know from the doctor's office was whether they could direct me to a Dr Poe equivalent in Britain. A few days later a name was produced. It felt like striking gold, and indeed that's what it was. Mr Bradford, a senior consultant based in Oxford, who had spent a year in Boston on a fellowship. His website informed me that he had achieved the gold medal for the highest score in his final ENT examination. I laughed when I read it.

I decided to pass on the Dundee trip, when the appointment letter finally showed up a month later.

4

THE BIG REVEAL

I understood that doctors needed to keep a sufficient distance for clear judgment, what the sociologist Renée Fox has termed detached concern, but I was beginning to wonder whether empathy was drummed out of some of them in their training. It seemed to me that both sides would benefit if they were able to put themselves in the patient's shoes. There had been many moments, over the preceding two and a half years, when I'd longed to air my thoughts.

'I'd like to see you cope with these symptoms, in a sleep-deprived state from attending to all the needs of your disabled son, running a business from home, helping your daughter progress through school, and managing everything in the household.'

But of course I didn't. Apart from the matter of sheer politeness (my manners were deeply instilled by my mother at an early age), there was always the danger that any of them might turn round and suggest I find another doctor. The necessity of keeping the doctor, any doctor, on my side was clear from the outset. And as they didn't ask about my life, I didn't tell them. However, I wasn't convinced that this modus operandi was getting me very far, so at the end of the letter to Mr Wood I had chosen to include a revelation about my new home situation:

'My husband is now seriously unwell. He has an inherited kidney condition, and has been told he will have to start dialysis in the near future.'

Just when I thought things couldn't get much more difficult, they had. There were now three out of four members of our family striving against a serious affliction.

Quite a number of things need to happen to prepare for the home treatment choice of peritoneal dialysis, but the main one is the surgical insertion of a catheter, the pliable plastic tube that carries the dialysis solution in and out of the abdomen. Once the catheter is in, it's vital that everything is kept scrupulously clean. If any bacteria were to enter it, there would be a high chance of an infection called peritonitis taking hold. A kidney patient has to be on a carefully controlled diet, closely monitor their weight, blood pressure and temperature, have regular health checks, and follow a strict routine for the dialysis procedure. It is life changing, as well as life giving.

On a miserable wet and windy evening, after I had finished feeding Patrick his meal, I loaded him and his wheelchair into the car, and drove to the Royal Infirmary of Edinburgh to collect Hugh. It was starting to get dark and, by the time we had left the renal ward with the fragile patient, night had fallen. It was while driving home mostly along narrow, pitch-black country roads that I was left in no doubt how far I had deteriorated. On busy routes and at junctions, my frazzled brain battled to cope with the overload of fast-moving vehicles, flashing lights, and swishing windscreen wipers. On the minor roads, glare blindness from the headlights of oncoming cars brought me up short, almost sending us off course countless times. Patrick, as often, was in an excited state in the car, so his squawking, shrieking and hand clapping from the back seat added an unwelcome auditory dimension. We might as well have been traversing a tight-rope, the way we inched our way along those thirty-five miles, me clinging to the steering wheel like a limpet, my passenger bemoaning the time the uncomfortable journey was taking, and chiding me for every pothole that we dipped into. It was a journey through a special kind of hell.

December arrived, and I travelled on the train down to Oxford. The Radcliffe Infirmary, a hospital in the centre of the city, had existed since 1770 and now exemplified the faded glory of a public building being wound down for imminent closure. A new site was in the process of development. I found my way along the long, narrow corridors to the Department of Otolaryngology, and waited for Mr Bradford (doctor no.3). When he emerged, the confident, cheerful demeanour of this doctor was a happy departure from the baffled, furrowed brows of his professional colleagues. B for bright, disposition and brain power. A series of audio tests were undertaken, and then Mr Bradford asked me to lie down for an examination of my ears. As he passed comment on the fact that my grommet had now extruded, and my Eustachian tube was definitely not widely patent, I began to develop the uncomfortable feeling that my diagnosis was slipping out of reach. The consultant played his cards close to his chest. I was asked some more questions about my symptoms, and then requested to sit in the waiting room again.

When I returned to the room we'd started in, this time it was full of students grouped against the wall on one side. I felt a flutter in my stomach, as I had a nasty feeling they were there for a precise reason. Mr Bradford was standing opposite me, looking rather pleased. There was a bird-like quality about him with his beady eyes.

'Please sit down. Do you mind if these students are present while we have our conversation?' he asked me.

I shook my head, and so he continued. 'I have no reason to believe you have a patulous Eustachian tube. It's actually relatively easy to discern when that's the case, so I'm sorry you've had to travel all the way from Scotland for me to tell you. P.E.T is an unusual condition, but I have a strong suspicion that you may have something considerably more unusual.'

I took a deep breath, as it dawned on me I hadn't breathed while he'd been speaking. I could feel all the eyes of the students boring into me from the right, but I didn't turn to look at them. That's why they're here, I thought. He's about to do his big reveal, the patient suffering from something rare they've never seen before.

'Yes, I think you may have Superior Semicircular Canal Dehiscence Syndrome. It's a bit of a mouthful isn't it? I don't suppose you've heard of it before. It means you have a thinning, or complete absence, of a portion of the temporal bone overlying your superior semicircular canal. That's one of your balance canals. It's therefore important that you have a CT scan to examine the bone on the left side, and it would make more sense for that to be done in Edinburgh, rather than you coming down here again. I'd review the scan myself though.'

I couldn't really take in what he was saying. I hadn't come prepared for any diagnosis other than P.E.T, and this thing, whatever it was, had a very complicated name that I'd never seen or heard anywhere. I smiled awkwardly.

'And if the scan shows that I do have it, what happens then?' I asked. 'Can it be fixed with surgery, and would you be able to do the operation?'

At this point Mr Bradford, becoming more bird-like, pulled himself up, and pushed out his chest as though fluffing his feathers. He laughed, tossing his head back. Looking at his audience, he said, 'I wouldn't dream of it, there's hardly anyone brave enough to tackle it. There's a surgeon in Manchester I can refer you to if you wish, as he's done a few of these procedures already.'

Words failed me. I knew there were probably a hundred questions I should be asking, but the need to get away from the staring eyes, and alarmed expressions, was compelling. Mr Bradford's smiling face certainly wasn't helping; it seemed an insensitive way to warn of the dangerous surgery that might lie ahead. I made my escape, and headed straight for the hospital toilets that I'd passed on the way in. As soon as I was out of sight behind a locked cubicle door, the tears trickled down. They were tears of shock, tears of loneliness, tears of hurt pride, and tears of relief. Relief that, however bad it sounded, I might at last have come to the end of my search.

When the call came through in February, I wasn't in the house. To say it was an anti-climax would be an understatement. My husband's delivery of the news, that the scan had confirmed a tiny hole in the bone on the left side, was so prosaic he could have been telling me that the dog had just been sick and he'd cleaned it up. He looked up from the newspaper for a few minutes to assess my reaction, and I asked whether Mr Bradford had said anything else.

'Just that he would be writing to the Manchester man, as he knows that's what you want him to do,' he said.

I didn't exempt myself from criticism in this scenario. At some point, the two of us had started diverging along separate paths, and we now each had our own tribulations to contend with. If my husband had decided to step in, to help guide me through what had developed into a diagnostic maze, I would have been overjoyed. I expected him to know that I was floundering – the search had, after all, so far taken up nearly four years of my life. But it wasn't to be. A self-contained nature was part of my make-up, much like my father, and it perhaps also stemmed from the four-year age gap between me and my older sisters. I had grown accustomed to getting on with things on my own, and less accustomed to letting down my defences. First the arrival of Patrick and his development delay, and then the forty-five months (since the fateful Dutch flight) spent fighting for my own health, had no doubt entrenched those characteristics. It was almost as though I'd forgotten how to cry for help.

I had spent so much time scouring the internet for clues that, when I could at last put a name to my problem, I had little enthusiasm left for in-depth research. I did establish the basics though, if only to explain the condition to my anxious mother, who was now in her early eighties. She lived a long way south in Surrey, where I had grown up, so I explained it to her on the telephone.

'Superior Semicircular Canal Dehiscence Syndrome, usually abbreviated to SCDS. It was a man called Dr Lloyd Minor who discovered the condition. He's over in America, at The John Hopkins University School of Medicine, in Baltimore. And what's amazing is it was only in 1995 that he discovered it – that's just twelve years ago.'

'Oh dear, but why do you have it, Philippa?' my mother said.

'I'm afraid I can't answer that, Mummy. It seems to go right back to when I was a very small child. They think the developmental anomaly occurs during the first three years of life, through a lack of bone deposition. But just because someone has the anatomic defect doesn't necessarily mean they'll have any symptoms. There are apparently lots of people walking around without any problems. Something must have happened to me on that flight I told you about.'

Back in the 1990s, Dr Minor and his team in the Department of Otolaryngology had seen a couple of patients who were suffering from the same symptom – when they heard a loud noise, everything in the room appeared to jump up and down. Dizziness and extreme nausea accompanied it. Recalling a study of pigeons undertaken many years in the past, which had found a link between specific eye movements and damage to certain canals of the inner ear, the team took their research forward, and discovered a balance disorder caused by a tiny hole in the superior canal, the uppermost canal of the vestibular structure. In other words, yes, it was actually possible to have a hole in your head. Minor's team gave these openings the label botanists use to describe holes left behind from a burst seed pod – dehiscence.

For those who are symptomatic, as I most definitely was, the opening causes the balance canals in the inner ear to be abnormally activated, thus responding to loud sounds. This sound-induced vertigo is known as the Tullio phenomenon, in medical speak. Professor Tullio had discovered this cause and effect almost one hundred years earlier in Italy, when he drilled tiny holes in the balance canals of his animal subjects, and found they became dizzy when exposed to sound.

Ear pressure-induced vertigo, such as coughing, sneezing or straining, produces nystagmus – rapid, uncontrolled eye movements. Some years later I read Dr Minor's comment, 'Some of my first patients were referred to me by the hospital's psychiatrists. One man said he got dizzy when he sang in the shower. Another said he could hear the sound of his own eyes moving. I would later discover that these patients were experiencing symptoms coming from inside their heads – but not in the ways others might have supposed.'

The more I read about SCDS, the more things started to fall into place. The symptoms were astonishingly wide-ranging, and they also varied from one person to the next. The most attention-grabbing was actually one I didn't have. The muscles that move the eyes are connected to the bones of the skull, and there's an element of friction as the muscles move. Some people with SCDS can hear their own eyes scratching as they move from side to side, a disturbing phenomenon. My eyes clicked quietly when I opened and shut them, and I hadn't mentioned this to anyone as I assumed everyone's eyes did the same. I'd also just recently noticed my neck creaking.

I had denied it when Mr Wood (doctor no.2) asked me about tinnitus, but now I discovered that tinnitus took many forms, and the sound of my heartbeat pounding was causing the thumpings, and a change in blood flow near the ear, the swooshings. It was called pulsatile tinnitus. The feeling of fullness in my left ear, present since the flight, was apparently a common symptom, as was a low-frequency conductive hearing loss – as opposed to the permanent kind of hearing loss that Mr Sanderson (doctor no.1) had pointed out in my right ear. The autophony (literally self hearing) which had led me to P.E.T. and hence to Mr Bradford (doctor no.3), was what was making my voice sound unbearably loud, as it was reverberating around my head, and accounted for the severe discomfort I experienced when singing, or raising my voice. (For those unaffected by SCDS, covering your ears with your hands, and then talking, swallowing and singing, gives just a tiny indication of what has to be tolerated all the time. Remove the hands over the ears, and the difference will be clear.) There were innumerable everyday sounds to which I had become hyper sensitive, such as our spaniel barking, my daughter slamming her door in a tantrum, or the clattering of a spoon hitting the floor, and these could all be attributed to hyperacusis, another classic sign of the condition.

When I had anticipated an acoustic neuroma at the time of my MRI scan, the blurry vision hadn't been in my imagination after all. SCDS affects the eyes too, quite dramatically, and mine were often bouncing up and down in a disturbing way. Doctors call that oscillopsia. Nausea, fatigue and headaches are all part of the picture, manifestations I'd been tackling for months, and they primarily result from the body's efforts to cope with the onslaught. The extent to which sufferers are affected by dizziness was the aspect to which I should have given very careful consideration. Had I done so, I might not have missed a link between SCDS and my pre-Amsterdam life.

My reading about the condition indicated that patients could have little or no balance complaints or, at the other end of the spectrum, have their lives completely dominated by them. I knew that in my case the situation was heading in the latter direction. The disequilibrium, with which the world became a slowly rocking boat, was regularly being intermixed with much more uncontrollable dizziness. I realised I had been using the term vertigo far too loosely, usually to explain to my family why I didn't want to climb to the top of tall structures, and admire the view. The true definition of the word is a sensation of rotation, or movement of one's self or of one's surroundings, in any plane, and it was clear that I was now encountering this true form far too frequently.

Shortly after my Oxford consultation I attended a Christmas party. I was hesitant, but I'd been persuaded by Fiona that it would be an enjoyable and, most importantly from my point of view, sit-down occasion. She had been the chair of the parent management committee for the Special Needs Playscheme for several years, and I had recently been appointed secretary. The local community centre held the yearly event to extend thanks to all its volunteers by providing a buffet meal, liquid refreshment, and musical entertainment. Hugh now had his dialysis arrangements underway, and always had to complete an evening session as soon as he got home from work. By the time I'd dealt with the children's usual bedtime routine, and then made myself presentable in a silk shirt and black trousers, I knew I was running late.

I rushed up the steps into the community centre, the sound of my feet booming in my ears. Clive, the centre's manager, was taking coats and I stalled, making idle conversation with him for several minutes. Nervousness was rearing its ugly head, as I could hear the noisy bustle from the other side of the velvet curtain that had been pulled across the hall doorway. I gave myself a silent pep talk: 'You just have to catch sight of the playscheme parents, make your way to their table, sit yourself down, and then everything will be fine.' There were regrettably two things I hadn't banked on – the coloured, strobe-like lights flickering around the walls, giving the bare hall a much-needed Christmassy atmosphere, and Kirsten, the playscheme coordinator, accosting me as soon as I crossed the threshold.

'Hello, Philippa. I'm glad you could make it. Did you have trouble getting away – how's Patrick?' She had to shout a little to make herself heard over the noise of the assembled guests, and a piano playing.

Tonight, with the overhead lights dimmed, Kirsten seemed to be attired in bright, twinkling stars that danced all over her body, and she'd become abnormally fuzzy around the edges. While I attempted to get her into focus, she continued, 'Let me introduce you to Councillor Innes. He's always been very supportive of the playscheme, and I know he'd like to talk to one of the mothers.'

And then the vertigo took hold in earnest. Councillor Innes was swirling, Kirsten was swirling, the rows of tables festooned with sprigs of holly and wineglasses, they were all swirling. A conversation was now an impossible feat – it was a miracle I was still standing. In a split second I had registered Fiona among the group sitting at the table furthest away, and I knew I had to reach my safe haven.

'I'm going to have to sit down, Kirsten. You know I've been having a lot of trouble with my ear,' I mumbled.

Seconds later, a stooped robot, staring straight ahead, was seen shuffling its way thirty yards down the aisle dividing the rows of tables, past all the seated committee members. It sat down at the furthest table, and didn't move, even for the buffet.

In Scott McCredie's book *Balance*, he describes Cheryl, a woman for whom walking had become an act of will: 'She had to be constantly vigilant about where she was in space, to *think* about how she was going to get from one point to the next. Assuming what she describes as a "Frankenstein" gait, her body stiff and rigid, her stance wide to compensate for her instability, Cheryl had to keep her gaze focused on the ground in front of her, to minimise visual distortion, looking up only to make sure she wasn't going to run into anything.'

I had become Cheryl, and what's more, I was now starting to resemble my son in motion, a boy with severe and complex special needs.

5

I CAN'T GO ON LIVING LIKE THIS

Manchester Piccadilly station is an important hub of the British railway system. The large, open concourse presented an immediate challenge on my arrival in May 2007 – just to get across it, and out through the exit on the far side. But I was in a determined mood. A further five sluggish months had been endured, and now I was on my way to meet the surgeon who was going to get me well again. We had enjoyed a spell of warm, sunny weather in East Lothian, and I had a healthy glow from the planting I'd been doing in our large front garden, where a new, ramped path had been laid, to enable easy access up and down to the house with Patrick. I had inherited my tall height, and my unruly, wavy brown hair, from my father, but also a skin that bronzed easily when exposed to sunlight. I strode along in my jeans and striped shirt, and hailed a taxi to take me to my destination. I had only been to the sprawling city once, years ago, for a university interview, and I didn't have time to negotiate its bus routes.

The hospital was on a much grander scale than its cousin in Oxford, but it too had seen better days. The clinic waiting area was chock-a-block with patients and their family members, but I squeezed into a space, and listened carefully for my name to be called for a hearing test. I seemed to be straining hard to catch all the sounds in the audio assessment, so my instinct told me things had worsened in the intervening period.

I don't know exactly what I had envisioned, but Mr Ingram (doctor no.4) didn't live up to it. His slight build and mild-mannered reserve didn't tie in with the words still ringing in my ears, 'hardly anyone brave enough to tackle it'. I must have subconsciously created a mighty Viking-style warrior in my mind, one ready to do battle with his scalpel. This doctor came across as a man of few words, and he wasn't going out of his way to put me at ease. I for impenetrable. Once we had got past the usual examination of ears, and a discussion about symptoms, Mr Ingram threw me completely off my guard.

'As you know, Mr Bradford has referred you as a patient with a dehiscence in the superior semicircular canal on the left side,' he said. 'I've been looking at the scan done in Edinburgh, and I'm not sure that I agree with him.'

I looked at him in amazement.

'I don't know what to say. I didn't think there was any doubt about what the scan had showed. I don't quite understand what you're telling me.'

'I'm not convinced at this stage that you have a hole in the canal, but it's possible that part of the problem is the quality of the scan,' he explained. 'The scanning we do here has a higher resolution, and the images are more defined.' He paused, clearly unsure what to do next. 'I think I'll take you round to the radiography department myself, right away. Have you got the time for them to do another scan this afternoon?'

Fortunately I did have the time, as I was booked into a local bed and breakfast place for the night, and so I trailed after the consultant, hurrying along the warren of corridors until we reached a reception desk, and a row of chairs lined up against the wall. Mr Ingram disappeared to talk to the radiographers.

When he came out a few minutes later he said, 'They're going to fit you in as soon as they can. Once it's done, make your way back round to my clinic again. We'll have another talk.'

By now I knew that a CT scan was quicker than an MRI, and didn't involve the same deafening noises; the relatively harmless, swishing sounds were ones I imagined I might hear in the unlikely event I ever got stuck inside a dishwasher. A couple of hours later a nurse showed me back into the consulting room, and this time she stayed in the room. I suspected it was unlikely Mr Ingram would have an immediate scan report on his desk, so it wasn't clear what we'd be talking about.

'I've decided I need to give your case some more thought, and wait for the results of the scan that's just been done,' he said. 'I'd like you to come back again, and we'll discuss the findings. I'll probably also want you to have a VEMP test next time. As I understand it from Mr Bradford, you haven't been experiencing any vertigo?'

I wanted to know what a VEMP test was, but there was a far more important matter to address. Not experiencing any vertigo, what was he thinking? I felt a mixture of annoyance and confusion – it was as though he hadn't been taking in anything I'd told him about my symptoms.

'No, I'm afraid that's not correct at all. It's over five months since I saw Mr Bradford, and my dizziness has been getting worse all the time. Just a couple of weeks ago I took my daughter to the cinema in Edinburgh, she's twelve. After the film we went to the café in John Lewis, the department store, and I literally couldn't move at one point.'

I paused to give him a chance to respond, but he just carried on looking at me.

'We had our food on a tray, and I couldn't walk from the till at the check out, across the crowded room to a table. The café was full of people with lots of noise, and Amy, my daughter, had to take the tray over to an empty table, and then come back and escort me. I had to hold onto her arm all the way, and walk very, very slowly. It was awful. I've no idea what I would have done if I'd been there on my own.'

My voice had started rising at the end of the outburst, and I could feel moisture accumulating in my eyes. Mr Ingram was still silent, and all of a sudden I could read his thoughts: This woman looks rather healthy with her sun tan, she doesn't seem to be in any particular distress, and she could probably cope perfectly well if I leave things as they are. Panic set in as I read his mind, and my words tumbled out in a hysterical fashion.

'I can't go on living like this. I don't just have a daughter. I also have a son who is very severely disabled. He can't do anything for himself. How can I go on looking after him, if I can barely look after myself? I have to keep putting myself in a horizontal position, just to relieve the pressure in my head. I lie down on the floor, anywhere, it's that bad. I'm at breaking point. I can't keep this up much longer.'

My voice crumbled, and a couple of tears broke free. I swiped them away – I felt cross with myself for getting upset, and cross with him for his apparent lack of feeling.

Mr Ingram's features softened a little, and he spoke at last.

'Well let's see how things turn out when we have the new scan back,' he said.

He opened up his diary, and started suggesting a date for the next appointment.

'I also have to work around my husband's renal dialysis, as he has to look after our son if I'm not there,' I added. 'He's now on a kidney transplant waiting list. But if you give me a date, I'll only contact you if it turns out I can't travel here that day.'

Mr Ingram looked as though I'd just slapped him. He glanced at the nurse, disbelief imprinted on his face. I had managed to convey some impression of the complex circumstances I was juggling.

When I returned two months later, I found the surgeon in a surprisingly different frame of mind. He informed me immediately that the new scan showed a strong likelihood that there was a hole, and he had arranged for the audiologist up on the fourth floor to undertake a special test which would hopefully decide things one way or the other. As a companion for this adventure, he introduced me to the other doctor in the room, who was working alongside Mr Ingram on a temporary secondment.

We made our way upstairs, and the audiologist explained what was going to happen to me. She had a soothing way of talking, and I relaxed, feeling I was in the hands of someone who knew what she was doing, and would try her best not to hurt me.

'Vestibular evoked myogenic potential technique is what VEMP stands for,' she said. 'I will be sitting here at the computer, and I need you to lie on the table on the other side of the glass screen. Please lie flat, but keep your head raised off the table for the duration of the test. I'm going to put these surface electrodes on your neck, and they'll pick up any muscle activation in that area. At the same time I'll be sending some loud clicks into your ear through these headphones. A person with SCDS will show increased sensitivity to sound. We'll do one ear at a time, starting with the right ear. Each side will take a few minutes. Dr Brown is going to stay in the room with you. Is that all ok? Just tell me when you're ready.'

It did sound ok, but once the process began I realised it wasn't as easy as I thought it would be, to keep my head raised up off the table, and my body still. My neck and shoulders were straining. The few minutes seemed incredibly long ones, but Kate at last waved to indicate I could rest, while she set things up for the left ear. We began again, and within seconds I was in deep trouble. My neck was already aching, but that was the least of my problems. The small room's grey walls were actually moving, and as I looked upwards in the hope of finding a stationary surface to focus on, I found instead a bright white ceiling that was spinning out of control. Round and round and round, faster and faster, I'd never experienced anything like it. I wanted to put my head back down on the table immediately, but Dr Brown stopped me saying, 'Please hold on, keep your head up, you mustn't put it down. You're doing really well. Just keep going, it won't be much longer.'

The few kind words were like a switch, and tears began streaming down my face. I didn't know what to do; I so desperately wanted the spinning to stop, and yet I knew I had to get to the end of the test. I hung my arms down at the sides of the table, and wrapped my fingers around the edges, to stop myself being thrown off. The queasiness in my stomach had fast developed into full-blown nausea.

'Can you hold on just a little longer?' he asked me.

I wobbled my head back and forth to answer, and he leaned towards me in a reassuring way. The tears were still pouring out, and now the motion sickness was in full control. I was struggling to breathe, I knew I would have to escape from the nightmare any second, it was unbearable.

Kate waved again.

'It's finished,' said Dr Brown. 'You can lie flat now. Shall I get a pillow for your head? Take as much time as you need – I can see you found that extremely difficult.'

I flopped back onto the table, and my body shuddered with relief. It was over. A wave of gratitude washed over me. It was Dr Brown's caring attitude that had made it bearable.

When I encountered Mr Ingram again, about an hour later, I seemed to be in the presence of a different man. Excitement was in the air. The results of the VEMP test had been conclusive, and now the talk was of surgery dates, not doubts about the diagnosis. He and Dr Brown conversed animatedly about SCDS, and the ins and outs of various tests and scans, but I may as well not have been in the room. I felt like a guinea pig, one that was of course essential to the experiment, but that need not be closely involved in the decision-making process. An alarm bell should have been ringing, particularly when Mr Brown departed, and my surgeon looked at me intently across his desk.

'I have so far seen fifteen people with SCDS, and I've operated on ten of them,' he said. 'I would like to do the operation a different way, when I do your surgery. I've been discussing the procedure with a colleague in Canada, and he's had very good success with it. It involves considerably less risk, and the operation is over much more quickly. Of course I would need your permission to do that.'

He had put me on the spot. I fidgeted in my seat, and looked down at my knees. I just wanted an operation. I wasn't in a position to offer an opinion about how he should carry out the operation, and I also doubted he was expecting any dissension.

'Does it mean you'd be trying it out on me for the first time?' I said. 'Is it very different to what you've done before? I haven't had a chance to tell you, but I talked to Lloyd Minor on the phone in May – has *he* ever done the operation that way?'

I wasn't inventing this. A conversation had taken place, by arrangement with Dr Minor's secretary, and he had seemed genuinely interested to hear from a patient across the Atlantic. My research instinct had, somewhat belatedly, been the driving force behind the call, as it seemed wise to go directly to the source of SCDS knowledge, to talk to the man who had identified the disorder. I made enquiries about Mr Ingram, and whether he had the best track record among surgeons in my country. Unfortunately Dr Minor hadn't known the answer to that.

Mr Ingram's eyebrows rose upwards slightly at the mention of Lloyd Minor, but he moved on smoothly.

'I can't give you an answer to that I'm afraid, although I have met Dr Minor. Regarding the method I intend to employ, much of it would be along the same route that I use regularly for other ear operations. It's just the last little stretch, further into the inner ear, which would be new territory.'

It was a date that I was after, and once it was produced, only three months away, the last little stretch suddenly seemed insignificant. I felt even luckier, when reference was made to another patient who had holes on *both* sides of her head. After one surgery she had lost some hearing, something Mr Ingram was at pains to stress happened only rarely, and because of that he was reluctant to agree to operate on her second ear. I departed from the hospital, delighted with my October date and full of pity for the poor, unknown woman who was afflicted with a doubly holey head.

The station concourse again threatened to topple me, as I made my way across it to the train heading north. The live departure boards were a no-go zone for my gaze, unless I stood completely still, and very gradually tilted my face at an angle to read them, without moving my head to the left or right. The very slightest wrong move could instigate a major spinning attack, and I would be frozen on the spot or, worse still, collapse on the ground in the midst of all the travellers rushing hither and thither. Once safely seated on the train, I mulled over the day's events, and then considered my unbalanced life. There was a question which was starting to prey on my mind – at what point had things begun to go awry? Was the flight, over four years ago, the only trigger and, if so, why had I been unsteady so many times before that?

I had a long train journey ahead of me, and my thoughts settled on the old Reading Room in the British Library, in London. The splendid, circular room was a masterpiece of mid-19th-century technology, and was believed to have been inspired by the domed Pantheon in Rome. A number of book stacks made of iron were built surrounding the room, and there were three miles of bookcases, and twenty-five miles of shelves. I had become familiar with the building early in my twenties, when I was working as a picture researcher and editorial assistant for Orbis Publishing. Our offices were a short walk away from the library. With my special pass for research purposes I made regular visits and then, for a period of several months, I was there every single morning. I had taken a fairly unusual degree in Ancient History, Archaeology and Latin, and it was why I had been selected by the managing director as a suitable candidate for fact checking, and general editorial input, for a book entitled *Sport and Games in the Ancient World*. It was in the process of being written by one of his fellow countrymen in Czechoslovakia.

It was a dream job for me – the freedom to work away from the office on my own initiative, an interesting subject I felt familiar with, and a beautiful setting for my quiet study periods. As the trolleys trundled around delivering books to the collection area, or returning them to shelves, the sounds echoed around the cavernous space, like claps of distant thunder. When readers pulled out or replaced the huge bound catalogues from the shelves, to search for the publications they wished to view, the noises of those great tomes being manoeuvred also bounced around the vast interior. As the days wore on, I felt progressively uncomfortable in the environment. If I was sitting down at my desk, engrossed in my work, I could successfully blot out the background hubbub, but I frequently had to make my way to the central collection area. It wasn't long before I dreaded those walks. I had to mentally prepare myself for each short journey. Once I was standing up, I needed to remain there for a moment, and then refocus. I had to find my centre of gravity before stepping forward, and once on the move, it was imperative I concentrated very hard and got to my destination quickly, so that I could safely prop myself up against the tall, wooden catalogue stands. It required the same preparation and consolidation of effort to get back to my desk seat. I couldn't make sense of these episodes. I seemed to be undergoing some sort of anxiety attack each time, but I had no idea why. Was the Reading Room walk an earlier, and less pronounced, manifestation of the Christmas community centre robotic shuffle?

My thoughts then jumped a short distance (same time frame) to High Holborn, less than a mile away from the British Library. The great thoroughfare had once been the main road from the Old City of London to the west. Many times in the 1980s, during my years of London office working, I had reason to wander up or down this busy street in the capital's centre, with its hotchpotch of modern and historical buildings, shops and cafés. There was one particular occasion though, which caused me such alarm that I hastily arranged a visit to a doctor soon after it. I was heading down on foot towards Waterloo

Bridge, to cross the Thames to the train station on the far side. I was forced to abandon my plan. Halfway down the busy road with its steady flow of buses, taxis and cars in both directions, I became so unbalanced I could no longer keep walking along the wide pavement. I slowly shifted sideways across to the right hand side, conscious of members of the public eyeing me suspiciously, no doubt wondering whether I was the worse for drink or drugs. I then continued to edge my way along the street, with one hand patting the wall of the tall building to which I was adjacent. It gave me the security I required. I carried on for a while in this fashion, virtually hugging the solid structures, and willing myself forward, little by little. It was a tiring, slow, not to mention ridiculous, way to advance, and the feeling of unsteadiness wasn't receding. I tried stopping for short breaks, and then progressing a little further, but eventually I admitted defeat. I waved my free arm to stop a passing taxi, and climbed into it. When I explained the unnerving incident to the GP, I found little sympathy. As he couldn't find anything wrong with me, he shrugged his shoulders and suggested that perhaps I should make an arrangement with the nurse for my ears to be syringed.

Over twenty unsteady years had passed since the treacherous High Holborn trek, and in just a few months' time I would know whether my dizziness had been conquered once and for all.

6

THE FIRST REPAIR

I was going to be in hospital for a week, and my mother was adamant she would visit me every day, afternoon and evening. First and foremost that was because she was my mother and, however irrational it may have been, she held herself partly responsible for the fact that I had something very wrong, very unusually wrong, with my head. Nothing I said changed that. She suspected, which was true, that my husband would need to stay in Scotland to help with the care of Patrick and to keep his home dialysis programme on track, but it was also because I was her baby, the youngest of her three daughters. I would have felt exactly the same – the need to be close at hand, for my own comfort as well as my child's. We had always had a good relationship, and she simply wanted to be there for me, in the same way she had been as I was growing up. She had not worked outside the home once she was married.

Moreover, my mother was one of life's worriers, and the worrying had been on the increase since she'd been on her own. My father was eighteen years older than her, and had died in 1987. There was no doubt in anyone's mind that she'd be worrying more, if she couldn't be near me after a major operation. For someone in their eighties she was in remarkably good health, but she was hard of hearing, and certainly less sprightly than she had been even just a couple of years before. It was fortunate that the Manchester hospital had a room available in their residential accommodation for relatives, so she would be within walking distance, and could be with me during all the visiting hours. We reached a compromise too – she wouldn't arrive on the first day. I suspected I might not be in a very good state immediately after having had my head opened up, and that would only upset her.

Early evening mid October, Hugh pulled into the drop-off zone at Edinburgh airport. Both children were in the back of the car, and they were all heading straight home for bedtime routines, or dialysis. Kisses and goodbyes were exchanged, and I tried to preserve a brave face for my daughter as she wished me luck, and told me not to worry. Our roles had been reversed. In my mind I was now the vulnerable child, at least that's how I felt as I wandered through the airport entrance, my family watching me from the car. A husband and wife belong together at challenging times, and had I not been so intent on coping I would have insisted on it. It was too late to rectify that. I concentrated on looking beyond the morning's surgery, to a life with renewed vigour on the far side, and if I found my thoughts drifting in a negative direction, I pulled the focus back to this goal. It was, after all, what I'd been striving for all along – to get myself diagnosed, and then find the appropriate treatment.

The first test was how to lighten the mood of the overnight stay in my gloomy hotel. I had selected it precisely for its inexpensiveness, as well as its proximity to the hospital, since I needed to be there for admission first thing in the morning. There were no on-site facilities, so I had purchased the contents of my evening meal at the airport, all of which needed to be consumed well before midnight, to keep within the restrictions related to the next day's general anaesthetic. I spread out my picnic on the patterned bedcover, in the clean but slightly shabby room: prawn mayonnaise sandwiches, a bag of salted crisps, one banana and a chocolate bar. Then I unscrewed the top on my mini, single-serving bottle of Chardonnay, and fetched the tumbler from the bathroom – I really know how to live it up, I thought to myself. Some mindless entertainment on the television kept me company, and I flicked my way through a magazine. I planned to stay awake as late as I could; I was anticipating a night of fitful sleep.

My bed on the hospital ward was the closest to the nurses' station. I could see them, and they could see me. It was reassuring to be near enough to catch their attention, but how concerned should I be that they deemed it necessary to keep such a watchful eye on me? As if to address this question, Mr Ingram hobbled into view in his surgical scrubs, one of his feet in a bulky brace. I knew that he'd suffered an ankle injury, as my surgery date had had to be put back, but I wasn't expecting to see him in such a compromised state. His secretary had described him as 'raring to get back to work'. He drew the privacy curtain halfway around the bed.

'Good morning,' he said.

'Good morning. How is your foot? I was very sorry to hear what had happened,' I replied.

'It's fine, thank you. Just slightly annoying now, but I won't have any trouble working the drill, so you don't need to worry,' he said with a smile. 'Before I ask you to sign this form, I'll quickly run through what's going to happen this morning. I shall be making a two-inch incision behind your left ear, creating a channel through the bone there which is called the mastoid, locating the balance canal where the problem lies, and using a paste made from your own bone to create a seal around the defect. Do you have any questions you'd like to ask?'

'No, nothing about the operation, thank you. But I did want to mention something strange that's been happening. I've been getting a sort of squelching feeling here.'

I pointed to the area below my ear, and under the jawbone.

'It's rather like having a tiny piece of bubble wrap there, which I can press on to release either liquid or air – I'm not sure which, to be honest. I think it's connected to the fact that, for months now, I've been making a gurgling noise in my sleep, as though I'm suctioning something down my throat. Both my husband and my daughter have commented on it, but of course I'm asleep so I don't really know what I'm doing.'

Mr Ingram stared at me. I expected him to question me further about this peculiar sensation, but he replied, 'I don't know what that could be. Now, the good news is you won't have to go into the intensive care unit. I'm carrying out a craniotomy on an older lady in the bed opposite you, and in the past that's how I would have done an SCDS surgical plugging. I'll be doing that operation before yours, and she'll have to be in ICU for the night. Once you're back up on the ward again this afternoon, I'll come and see how you are.'

The woman and I had already exchanged morning greetings from our beds, and now that I knew about the serious nature of her condition I made sure to extend my good wishes, as she was wheeled out of the ward. A craniotomy is the surgical removal, and subsequent replacement, of part of the bone from the skull, thereby exposing the brain. I had narrowly escaped one.

Mr Ingram kept his word, and came to the side of my bed later in the day. I was feeling very groggy, and our conversation was brief.

'The procedure went very well indeed, and I was impressed with the time it took,' he told me. 'You were in theatre for about an hour and a half, and that's much quicker than the other repairs I've carried out.'

He seemed animated and relaxed, probably glad to have the experiment behind him. The same could not be said for me. I was relieved my mother wasn't visiting, as I would have been unable to talk to her. There was a large amount of pain, my head felt like a lead weight, and I could sense it was only a matter of time before I needed to be sick. That time arrived in the middle of the night. Whether the anaesthetic was the cause, or general post-surgery trauma, I wasn't sure. There was absolutely no question of eating anything, and I had to force myself to keep sipping water, encouraged by the nurses to do so. Nothing seemed better at that point, everything seemed worse.

'Hello. Have you just been asleep? How are you? Have you had your lunch?'

It was surprising that was my mother's third question rather than the first, as she had what was verging on an obsession with food – not eating it, but making sure others were eating it. I stretched out my arms to greet her. I hadn't the heart to tell her I couldn't possibly consume anything. I had tried at breakfast, and only managed to nibble a corner of a piece of toast. The nausea was still all pervasive. I was going to have to be economical with the truth during her visits. While she was there, I made a first attempt to walk from my bed to the bathroom, which was all of thirty yards past the nurses' station. I held onto her slim body, and tentatively stepped forward. The dizziness was severe. It worried me that we would both fall down if she couldn't support me, so I gestured to one of the nurses for help. We slowly made the journey there and back, and it was now evident how incapacitated I was. I hadn't been warned to expect such a severe decline.

Mr Ingram paid another quick visit mid week, which was unexpected and I was grateful for it. When my mother arrived for her afternoon sit with me, I wrote down an account of what he'd said. We now scribbled in a notebook any significant or secret exchanges. I had bandages around my partly shaven head, and heaven knows what else stuffed in my ear, and my mother's hearing was long past its best, so I devised this scheme to prevent a lot of shouting at each other, for all to hear on the open ward. My mother seemed unable to judge the volume of her own voice, and had already let loose some unsavoury remarks about the number of 'foreign' doctors, as well as asking probing questions about the state of other patients' health. I also found it tiring to talk, so we would often pass the time playing noughts and crosses in the notebook, or hangman, a game I loved from my childhood. It was comforting to have my mother with me.

'He reassured me about all the pressure that's still in my head, and said it will be four to six weeks before I know whether all the symptoms have gone,' I wrote. 'He told me the procedure of closing off one of my balance canals will have caused a lot of blood and fluid to clog up my ear, and so he's not surprised I have so much pressure at the moment. I did explain to him that it's extremely muffled, and feels full of cotton wool on that side. He still thinks it's ok for me to go home on Saturday – I'm supposed to rest for six weeks, and not bend over, or do any lifting.'

The idea was that my mother would convey the message to Hugh on the telephone, as he would be driving down from Scotland to come and take me home. What my mother didn't know was the extent of the pain I was experiencing. On one evening visit, however, she arrived early, and caught me quietly sobbing on my bed, curled up in a foetal position. The increasing agony as the week wore on, and the continuous nausea which had only marginally reduced, had got the better of me. One friendly nurse expressed concern about my requests for stronger and stronger painkillers, but my crying had been triggered by another, less compassionate one, informing me curtly that it was far too soon for a further dose of morphine to be administered.

I blurted it all out to my mother.

'Each time I inform the registrar, or any of the junior doctors, about how much everything hurts, when they're doing the morning rounds, they just don't seem to be taking notice of what I'm telling them. They nod, and say they'll pass it on to Mr Ingram, but when I look at the notes – the ones in the folder at the end of the bed – it always says "doing fine". But I'm not doing fine.'

I paused, trying to halt the next flow of tears issuing from frustration.

'My head is about to burst, and I'm absolutely worn out with it all. The only thing that I think might be slightly better is the autophony – you know, the loud noises like my voice booming inside my head. Everything else is ten times worse, and I can barely get to the bathroom and back on my own.'

I was already beginning to regret my outburst, as my mother looked so worried. I could also see the conflict in her face, torn by her unwavering confidence in anyone with the title of doctor, and the anxiety about her daughter.

'Is it getting a little easier to walk now? Does a nurse have to help you every time?' she asked.

'They always watch like hawks if I get up off the bed, and usually ask me if I need help, but I am doing it on my own now. It's very difficult though. The physiotherapist came again this afternoon, and he's given me some exercises to work on at home.'

I perked up momentarily, remembering the conversation. 'He said Mr Ingram was not a man of many words. So it's not just me that's noticed that. But I told him that when the surgeon last came to talk to me he was quite chatty. The physio man smiled and said, "Well, that's because you're a nice lady I think." That was sweet of him, wasn't it?'

My mother took my hand. 'You *are* a nice lady,' she said. That set off the crying again.

On Friday I felt more positive, as departure day was imminent. On one of my precarious bathroom strolls I encountered the craniotomy patient, who hadn't been on my ward since her operation. She looked bright and cheerful, with no sign of unsteadiness.

'How did everything go? You're looking very well, and very happy,' I said to her.

'Yes, thank you. I feel very well, so much better. I had to wait several months for the operation, but it's been well worth the wait – I feel like a different person,' she said.

'That's marvellous. Do you mind me asking what was wrong with your head?'

'Oh, it's rather an unusual thing, a bit like having a leaking roof.' She laughed. 'I had fluid that was escaping from around my brain. Mr Ingram has fixed it though. Are you getting on alright?'

My inclination was to reply, 'Not half as well as you.' But instead I said, 'I think I'm going to have to be patient. I'm very dizzy, but I'm told everything will take a while to settle down. Good luck when you go home today.'

I tottered back to my bed, and mulled over our chat. Wasn't there something a bit odd going on here? Things seemed to be back to front. My hospital acquaintance had just come through some dangerous brain surgery unscathed, and was now as right as rain. I hadn't, and I wasn't.

As luck would have it, the motorway had exceptionally heavy weekend traffic on our way back northwards. We stopped en route at a motorway service station, my first experience in a bustling environment since the operation. I clung onto my husband, as we wandered through to the crowded café, my head now bandage free. I still had the stitches in, and there was a small, bald patch around the wound, mainly hidden by my matted hair. The over stimulation in the large room was paralysing to start with, because of so many extraordinarily tinny noises bouncing around the room, and loud, popping sounds in my ear. I tried my best to tune out all the interference. It was the battlefield of the busy ladies toilet that very nearly defeated me. I had entered a war zone. The hand dryers blasted out, the feet coming and going were like rifles clattering, cubicle doors banged and clicked, spurts of water from running taps whizzed like rockets, and the flushing toilets were minor explosions. I steadied myself against the wall before exiting, and then made a dash for the door.

My niece Alice, the daughter of my eldest sister, had offered her support for several days once I was home. Apart from my physical restrictions, her presence was extremely welcome, as we always enjoyed each other's company. I couldn't stop thinking about the brain fluid I'd been told about. I had no idea it was possible for the head to spring a leak like that – first holes, and now leaks. I obviously had a lot to learn. Every available minute I scoured the internet, trying to understand exactly what had been wrong with the craniotomy patient, and at last I found what I was looking for. If there was a tear in the membrane surrounding the brain and spinal cord, it resulted in the escape of cerebrospinal fluid, usually referred to as CSF. Its thin, watery appearance belied its vital role in protecting the brain. Certain types of head surgery, or head injuries, were often the culprits in causing such leaks.

Bewildered Alice was subjected to my endless ruminations over whether this could account for my own unbearable head pressure, a major symptom before my surgery, and now considerably worse. Did it also provide a reason for the squelching bubble wrap phenomenon that had failed to grab my surgeon's attention when I'd mentioned it? While the children were at school, Alice and I made little excursions from the house. It was a stone's throw from a sandy beach looking north across the Firth of Forth, and a wooded area with grassland, and spiky sea buckthorn around the dunes. Alice took charge of Maisie, our energetic cocker spaniel, to ensure I wasn't pulled over, and I walked alongside, gradually building up strength, and retraining my balance system. It was during these short walks that I became aware of tiny drops of clear liquid falling from my left nostril, and the drips seemed more apparent when I was in a kneeling position, bent over to scoop up Maisie's deposits. This had definitely not been happening before my operation.

By the end of October, I was convinced there was sufficient evidence to raise the matter with Mr Ingram, particularly as he'd told me to get in touch if I needed to. I summarised everything for him in a fax, stressing that nearly two weeks on from surgery I was in a pretty bad way.

'I cannot stay upright for any length of time, as my head immediately feels as though it needs to burst open. My face becomes numb on the left side, and my hand starts tingling.' It was a long list of woes: intense pressure all over my head, and in my left ear; hearing loss, as well as crackling, popping, squishing, and squelching noises in the ear; intermittent headaches, always worse in an upright position; nausea, and blurry eyes. I reminded him as well that I had a frightening urge to close my eyes whilst driving the car, and that I was extremely sensitive to any bright light. I rounded it all off, lest he'd forgotten, with the two main traumatic incidents that had occurred – the flight and, at least a year before that, a serious blow to the head which Patrick had inflicted on me. While I was crouching to run the bath for him, he had reached over to the wall, and brought a heavy, metal handrail crashing down with full force onto my head, just as I was rising up to a standing position.

I wasn't surprised to receive a call from the consultant within hours. Apart from delivering some very unpleasant symptoms, a CSF leak puts a person in danger of contracting meningitis, a life threatening infection which affects the delicate membranes covering the brain, and spinal cord. I hadn't mentioned this to him, but we already had one serious infection in the household. Hugh had become very unwell from peritonitis, as a result of an oversight with his dialysis during his first night away from home, before collecting me in Manchester. Mr Ingram talked me through my ongoing symptoms, listening carefully, but at the end of the discussion he reiterated that it was very early days, and more time was needed to see how I progressed. The dreaded meningitis remained an unspoken word. Knowing what I knew about my potential risk, this seemed an unusual omission, but he did ask me to keep him informed of any further discharge. I wrote with more evidence two days later, but heard nothing in response.

It was exactly a fortnight after my arrival home that things took a turn for the worse. After having fed Patrick his evening meal, I was relaxing on a sofa, and had stretched myself out with my head on a cushion in an effort to release the pressure, and reduce the build up of pain. Out of the blue a panic attack, to top all panic attacks, took control. Everything in the room was swimming all at once, my ear seemed close to exploding, I was gasping for breath, and my heart palpitations were ferocious. I thought I might be about to faint. I very slowly drew myself upright again. I tried, and failed, to regulate my breathing.

'Hugh, Hugh. Please come quickly. I can't breathe properly. I need to see a doctor,' I shouted out. I was normally a very calm person, so the sight of my petrified face was enough to cause him alarm.

'What would you like me to do? Try to relax, and take slow, deep breaths,' he said. 'I can't take you anywhere myself, because of Patrick and my dialysis. Should I call an ambulance? If I do that, they'll almost certainly say they have to take you up to the Royal Infirmary.'

I was under no illusion about the amount of disruption that I was going to be causing, but I had no alternative but to be checked over by a qualified professional. I nodded my acceptance of his suggestion. Hours later, when I was being discharged from the main Edinburgh hospital late at night, having been given the all clear, politeness barely masked the condescension in the junior doctor's voice, as the words panic attack crossed his lips. He described the situation to my husband without suggesting any preventative measures to employ for the future. Neither the doctor nor Hugh needed to spell it out. I imagined what they were thinking – that I had to get a grip of things, and pull myself together. Our next door neighbours had had to come to the rescue, installing themselves in our house to ensure the safety of Patrick and Amy, while Hugh collected me. I felt guilty and innocent simultaneously.

November 21, the date of my post-op visit back in Manchester, didn't come a moment too soon. For the first hour it was just the audiologist and me. I had been told there was a twenty percent chance that my hearing might worsen with the operation, but Kate's thorough hearing test showed this hadn't happened. The VEMP test was repeated and, to my enormous relief, this time I wasn't sent into a spinning frenzy, which was an indication that the hole in the bone had been successfully tackled. As I found Kate generally sympathetic about my symptoms, I decided to broach the subject of the vicious bouts of vertigo that I kept experiencing.

'Kate, as the VEMP now looks relatively normal, do you have any idea why I'm still getting so dizzy?' I asked. 'It's happening frequently, when I lie down, or when I turn over in bed.'

'That sounds to me as though it's a direct result of what Mr Ingram did in the operation,' she said. 'There are calcium crystals within the labyrinth of the inner ear, and problems with dizziness can occur if those shift from their usual position. It's known as BPPV – benign paroxysmal positional vertigo. Mr Ingram will be here any minute, and then we can take a look at that together. We'll probably need to do some re-positioning manoeuvres to rectify it.'

Just as I was wondering why ear specialists had such a fondness for acronyms, the consultant walked through the door. He took off his raincoat, put down his leather briefcase, and apologised for the fact that he had been held up at the children's hospital. I immediately warmed to him, glad that the care of children came high on his list. Mr Ingram took the VEMP result as a sign that everything was in order, but I could see the smile fading away as I announced, 'I know this isn't what you want to hear, but I'm afraid I really don't feel better at all. The autophony seems to have gone, and that's wonderful, but that's the only thing that has improved.'

He asked me to lie on the table again, so that he could see whether it prompted more spinning.

'If it's alright with you, Kate and I are going to take a short video to record what's happening with your eye movements, and then I shall need you to put on these Frenzel goggles for me,' Mr Ingram said. 'If it seems necessary, we'll do a few manipulations which, Kate may have explained, should help with your dizzy spells. They're called Epley manoeuvres.'

Without hesitation, my prone position had the desired or undesired effect, depending on whether you were doctor or patient. I put on the goggles, and was transformed in an instant to a bug-eyed monster, from a science fiction setting. My heavy black, bulbous eye wear, tightened round the back of my head with rubber straps, prevented me from seeing out, while giving my examiners a magnified view of my darting eyes. I could tell from their excited exclamations that the directions of the eye movements were significant. They performed the exercises by taking hold of my head, rotating it to varying degrees, and turning me from side to side me in different positions.

Another of Kate's tests had shown an unusually high level of negative pressure in the operated ear, but the only remedy suggested for that was an especially strong decongestant spray. I was instructed to report back the results of its use in two weeks' time, and if there was no improvement a new MRI scan was to be arranged. The very mention of those capital letters made me shudder.

I wasn't remotely surprised that the spray made no difference, but what was more disturbing was that the manoeuvres hadn't helped either. Lying down, rolling over, or tilting my head just a little too far back, all continued to send me into a fast spin. I knew I now faced another long wait before the next scan. I had asked at my consultation whether the request could be processed urgently, but received a rapid put-down: 'Not unless you're willing to pay for it yourself.' An MRI scan costs hundreds of pounds, so I wasn't in a position to readily agree to that, and it wasn't just money that was at stake. Trust was eroding, the all important element in a doctor patient relationship. I was starting to doubt, in the same way as I had before the operation, whether my surgeon really understood the level of stress being caused by my symptoms.

I had little choice but to draw on my research skills in the intervening period, reading and noting any complications in similar case studies, and it wasn't long before I made a new discovery. First holes, then leaks, now tears. How many more types of imperfection could I unearth?

In between the air-filled middle ear and the fluid-filled space of the inner ear, very small, thin membranes act as little dividers. They are called the oval and round windows. A tear in one, or both, of these windows is termed a perilymph fistula, shortened to PLF – another beloved acronym – and it causes tiny amounts of perilymph fluid to escape from the inner ear. What particularly caught my eye about this type of flaw was that it was known to happen on flights. I read with eagerness a study from 2003, in which four cabin attendants from a single Scandinavian airline had been shown to have defects in this part of their ears, as a result of their flying jobs. This type of ear damage was referred to as barotrauma, and was something that divers had to be equally wary of. The invisible damage could cause very debilitating symptoms, most commonly affecting balance, and creating a feeling of fullness in the ear. Furthermore, my investigative work told me that perilymph fluid was connected to the CSF around the brain, so once again the risk of meningitis reared its head.

I'd heard it promulgated that doctors should reveal information to their patients on a need-to-know basis, but this was starting to get ridiculous. Dialogue from *Yes, Prime Minister*, one of our well-loved comedy television programmes, came to mind: 'So that means you need to know things, even when you don't need to know them. You need to know them, not because you need to know them, but because you need to know whether or not you need to know. If you don't need to know, you still need to know, so that you know that there is no need to know.' Indeed I do, I thought – yes to all of those.

Two more pieces of correspondence, and two phone calls, one from my husband and another from a GP, failed to elicit a response from Mr Ingram. Nobody responds well to being ignored but in my case, perhaps fortunately, it only made me more determined to get the answers I sought. Kate, by contrast, proved to be an excellent correspondent, and readily confirmed by email that she had the necessary equipment to undertake the fistula test I enquired about. We exchanged notes about how the test needed to be performed to ensure an accurate result, as it was not one that she'd done before.

When, at long last, an appointment date of January 16 materialised, I made my now familiar, lengthy train expedition back to the hospital. Kate's news that Mr Ingram had called in that morning with a cold, and was staying at home, left me lost for words. His absence did, however, leave us free to pursue our plan and, closely following the guidelines we'd gathered from the internet, we set up the test which involved applying pressure into the ear. The bug-eyed monster goggles were put to good use – Kate clearly detected the eye movements she was looking for, confirming a positive result. We did it again, just to be sure. Mission accomplished, I hurried downstairs for my MRI scan. It was considerably less upsetting than my first experience in a scanning tunnel two and half years before.

As Mr Ingram wasn't in the hospital to review the scan there and then, with me and the senior radiologist, I was assured that he would be in touch by telephone instead. Days passed, and I began to consider all the possibilities: Had he just forgotten to ring? Had he not recovered from his cold, and instead become more unwell? Was he so busy that there was no spare time in the day to make the call? When I picked up the phone at the very end of the month, and heard his voice, my heart leapt with anticipation. I was bursting to know what the scan had shown, and also to hear what he made of the positive fistula test. In a deadpan manner, my surgeon announced that the scan had revealed nothing wrong, and the surgery area looked fine.

'I can't explain your continued symptoms,' he said. No mention of the calls unreturned, the consultation missed, the positive fistula test, the dripping nose, or the worsening spinning attacks. No words of comfort.

'I'll send a letter to your GP. I think any further investigations should be made closer to your home, and perhaps a referral made to a neurologist.' Not even the name of a new consultant.

The events of the last four and a half grim years unravelled before my eyes. I slowly placed the receiver back on the phone. I was in shock.

7

LANGUAGE OF MEDICINE

I had effectively been cut adrift. One of a relatively small number of consultants that knew anything about my rare condition had just discharged me from his care. It took several days for the reality to sink in – I could hardly believe what had happened. Had I not been a natural optimist, and fortunate enough to have been endowed with an enormous capacity for hope, I would have been sunk. Hope is what keeps a person moving forward, and brings with it the strength to persevere through adversity. I knew I had to act on Albert Einstein's words: 'Life is like riding a bicycle. To keep your balance, you must keep moving.'

It was important to construct a plan of what to do next, but first I needed to find the energy and drive to get started. There were three essential elements that provided the drive: my son, my dog and music. Without my son, and his high level of need and dependence on me, I may never have found the impetus to keep striving for a return to good health. I simply had to get better for his sake – that had always been the case, and it remained so. Patrick gave my life a meaning and a purpose.

Maisie got me out of the house every day. The beautiful, Blue Roan field cocker spaniel had to have regular exercise, and that ensured I received mine as well, and thereby maintained my physical and mental wellbeing as much as was possible in the circumstances. The walks provided very important thinking time. My pet was there at my side in some very dark moments of isolation too, cheering me up with her playful antics, or gently resting her long, black nose on my chest. I really loved her. Research has proved time and again that dogs reduce stress, and improve the mood of their human companions.

It was music that lifted my spirits. Wherever I drove, music would accompany me in the car, and towards the end of the day, as I prepared what would often be a series of meals for the children, and later in the evening for my husband and I, the stress of the day would be relieved with well-chosen melodies. Classical, soul, rock, country, pop, it never failed to work its magic. It was better than any drug for me. I honestly couldn't have kept going without it.

Research conducted by the neuroscientist Valorie Salimpoor has backed up the view of the German poet Berthold Auerbach that 'music washes away from the soul the dust of everyday life.' Clear evidence was produced that music releases dopamine, the feel-good hormone, and it can generate not only a focus, but a reduction in anxiety. Jessica Grahn, another neuroscientist, believes that music can even reduce pain, or help people recover from injuries, as well as improving their cognitive skills. Daniel Abrams, a researcher at Stanford University School of Medicine, organised a study which revealed some interesting effects on participants listening to music while undergoing an MRI brain scan. The music had an almost identical effect within their brains, and it activated the regions connected with movement, planning, attention, and memory. Listening to music changes the brain chemistry – when you absorb the music that you like, it will put you in a good mood, motivate you, and propel you. And that's exactly what it had to do for me – propel me forward.

Having talked through the situation with a caring GP, she and I agreed that it was not a neurologist that I needed, but a very good ENT specialist, this time in Edinburgh. To that end, I contacted Mr Bradford back in Oxford. He showed his support by responding the same day, and leaving a detailed message on our answer machine, in which he expressed concern about my post-operative symptoms. He also left the name of a nearby doctor he could personally recommend. I wasted no time in setting up a private appointment, although I knew it could prove to be a risky strategy, as a patient hopping from the private side to the NHS, and back again, would be frowned upon. The same doctors worked in the two systems concurrently, and the private lists were predominantly comprised of those with health insurance. I didn't have any. Despite my calculated risk, it transpired that a wait of at least six weeks was still going to be necessary, as the consultant was holidaying on the other side of the world.

In the meantime, life had to carry on. I was still compiling my local business directory, but I had to reduce the frequency of its publication. I didn't have the energy reserves to put in the time and effort required to get the booklet ready every couple of months, which I'd been doing in the past. On the other hand, it was a means of retaining some sanity, re-establishing a day to day routine, and earning a small amount of money, so I was determined not to chuck it all in. I had had ambitions of setting up a website and widening the business, but those ideas had to be abandoned. The school week finished at midday each Friday, and my son returned home soon after three on the other days, so my time without him was very limited. Once Patrick was with me, he had to have my full attention.

That particular Thursday, March 20, I announced my arrival at the private hospital with some trepidation – I was on Mr Sanderson's (doctor no.1) territory again, and it wasn't bringing back happy memories. It was only a few months short of four years that the medical saga had had its unpromising start with that doctor, and a lot was hanging on this new one whom Mr Bradford had stressed was considerate and very experienced. I walked into his room, and a gentle face greeted me. A tall, slender man with greying hair offered his hand (doctor no.5).

'Hello, I'm Dr Kerr.' K for kindly, I hoped.

'Thank you for the letter you sent. I've just been reading it,' he said. 'I'm going to take a quick look at your head, but from everything you've told me, I think I need to see you urgently in my NHS clinic. This isn't the place for you – we need to get you back into the NHS system straightaway. What I really need access to, though, are all your notes from Manchester. Do you have those?'

'Thank you, Dr Kerr.'

I half closed my eyes, and considered the long version I could give him. First, they took over three weeks to get the notes into the 'copying department' to take copies. Now they're sitting with the consultant somewhere, waiting for him to sign them off – goodness knows why he has to do that, as it was his idea to refer me back up to Edinburgh. Then they have to let me know how much to pay, and then they'll send me the notes, by second class post of course. Now that's just the clinic and surgery notes, plus the audiology tests. The scans are all sitting in another section, waiting to be copied onto CDs, and they have to go through a separate procedure. It's a slow, crazy system, and no amount of telephoning, saying they are needed urgently, seems to make any difference. They just tell me they're allowed forty days to deal with it – it's a cheek, those are my personal records, and I can't get at them.

'No, I don't have them yet,' I replied. 'I did put in a request for them some weeks ago, and I'll chase it up again.'

'I was going to suggest you come and see me tomorrow, but of course it's Good Friday,' he said, looking at his diary. 'Could you come along next Wednesday morning instead? I'll get a letter sent out to you with the time. Allow a couple of hours, so we can do a thorough investigation. I'm afraid I'd better tell you this now, though. I'm about to retire, in six weeks' time.'

Six weeks. I wanted to scream.

'I actually don't think I would be the right person to sort everything out,' he continued, 'so it probably doesn't matter too much. I have another doctor in mind, who can take over from me.'

I saw Dr Kerr twice more, and by the second time he had a fat folder of my Manchester notes to wade through. He told me that it seemed very likely that I had a perilymph fistula, the tear in the middle ear, and that he understood the urgency of my situation. It would probably mean another surgery, to make the repair.

'No need to worry. I'll do a detailed referral letter, and stress the fact that you need to be seen as quickly as possible,' he confirmed. 'I'm going to give you these glucose sticks to take home with you, and I'd like you to test the nasal fluid, when you have a chance. Catch some of the drips on the end of the sticks, and see what colour they change to. Call up, and let one of the nurses know the results. Has anyone yet suggested that you try to collect some, to be sent away for testing? It's important that we find out whether it is in fact CSF, as I'm sure you understand.'

'Yes, Mr Ingram asked me to try,' I said. 'I posted him a tiny sample. But the trouble is the watery liquid just dribbles out in very small amounts, and then spreads around my nose. It's almost impossible to collect. The test came back negative, but I'm worried about that too. Mr Ingram didn't send me any instructions for collecting the liquid, or delivering the sample. He just said there needed to be one millilitre. When his secretary told me the test result was negative, I made quite a few enquiries myself. The laboratories I emailed all told me the same things. That there was a high risk of contamination, if the sample was collected from the nose; the sample had to be fresh, and tested immediately (or kept in a fridge for twenty four hours); and that there was a high false negative rate. In other words, it was extremely difficult to test, except in a hospital setting. And all I'd been asked to do was to send it in the post. There seems little hope of that sort of sample testing positive, would you agree?'

Dr Kerr looked at me. What I hoped to see in his expression was a clear understanding of my predicament.

'I'm not sure about that,' he said. 'See if you can collect another sample, and we'll send it away.' He handed me a plastic pot for the task.

I liked Dr Kerr, and I needed him to help me by putting me back on the right track. But his reply seriously troubled me. I had just given him some accurate information, direct from the laboratories that handled the relevant type of testing, and he was acting as though the words hadn't left my mouth. How was I ever going to establish whether I had brain fluid escaping, if the doctors didn't actually know how a test should be carried out?

My hopes had to be pinned on the next candidate. His name was Dr Miller (doctor no.6), and I returned to the depressing building to meet him two months later. My first impression was of another doctor not far away from retirement, with a polite, business-like manner. His opening statement was honest, but slightly concerning.

'I have only ever seen one patient with Superior Semicircular Canal Dehiscence Syndrome,' he told me. 'I've never carried out any operations for that condition myself, but I do know your surgeon in Manchester. If you don't mind, I'd like you to go back in time, and tell me how this all started.'

I found his request curious, as I had seen the informative letter that Dr Kerr had compiled for him, but I summarised how I had acquired the original diagnosis, and then I explained the operating stage. I wasn't getting the impression there was a strict time constraint, which would normally be the case in any NHS consultation, so I presumed we would shortly be discussing in depth what had been wrong with me since the surgery.

'Ok,' he said. 'Now I need to know exactly what the current symptoms are, and I'm going to ask you a series of questions, and type the answers into my computer. I have a questionnaire which I use for this.'

I was beginning to feel uncomfortable with his approach. My case was clearly a complicated one, and now he was about to condense my present situation into a series of questions and answers, to fit neatly into his boxes. Dr Nancy Angoff, at Yale School of Medicine, has described this as something patients witness all too often – the cold and depersonalising language and process of medicine. She has warned students to beware of it: 'Right now you are on the same side as your patients. And as you get halfway over the bridge you'll find yourself changing, and the language the patient had, and you had, is being replaced by this other language, the language of medicine. Their personal story is being replaced by the medical story. And then you find yourself on the other side of that bridge – you're part of the medical culture. When you get there, I want you to hold onto every bit of your old self, your now self. I want you to remember these patients.'

As the questionnaire proceeded, I had every reason to suspect that Dr Miller hadn't held onto his old self, his now self. We reached a point where the questions were irrelevant or misleading, and I attempted to explain this to him. I knew that if he didn't hear my proper story, there was little chance of making headway. If he just asked questions, he would just get answers, and nothing else. The best place to find the clue to a medical complication was surely in the unfolding of events, as Lisa Sanders has demonstrated in her book *Every Patient Tells a Story*. 'That story will often provide not only the whats, wheres, and whens extracted by an interrogation, but often the whys and hows as well.'

Dr Miller wasn't going to be deterred; he ploughed on, staring at his screen, and tapping the keyboard. I glanced at my watch, and realised I had been in his room for nearly fifty minutes. After he'd typed in the final answer, he swivelled round to face me. Then he dropped the bombshell.

'I am going to put you on some medication for the next three months – it's called Betahistine,' he said. 'Your symptoms suggest to me that you're suffering from the inner ear disorder endolymphatic hydrops, and you may have it quite severely. The pattern of your hearing tests fits in with that too. They don't look indicative of a perilymph fistula. It could take several months to get things under control, so I'll see you again in August.'

Yet again I'd been caught unawares. I had gone into the consultation hoping for the offer of a relatively simple operation to put me right, and I was leaving with a prescription for some pills that I didn't think were going to make the slightest difference. I had no medical training whatsoever, but by this time I had read an extensive amount about almost everything that could possibly go wrong with ears. I knew that endolymph was held within a sac inside the inner ear, and was maintained at a constant volume in normal circumstances. In an ear affected by hydrops, the volume and concentration of the endolymph fluctuated, and caused symptoms such as fullness in the ear, tinnitus, hearing loss, and dizziness. I had not read anywhere that it caused clear watery fluid to drip out of anyone's nose. If the consultant had indeed read Dr Kerr's letter, he must have seen too that the test strips I'd been given by Dr Kerr had shown a positive result for glucose in the nose drips – by no means a definitive sign for CSF brain fluid, but not one to be ignored either.

I took the piece of paper handed to me, and shook hands with Dr Miller. As if to add insult to injury, he added as an after thought that the back up plan might be to consider the possibility of migraine. Where did that idea spring from? I couldn't look him in the eyes. He would have seen my anger.

I started taking the pills later the same day. I had every intention of seeing whether his remedy worked, despite my doubts. Three weeks into the treatment, with no change, something significant occurred while I was at home with my daughter. It was a Saturday morning. Amy was standing close to me, describing a school project that she had to complete over the weekend, while I watered some indoor plants on a window sill. I put down the chrome watering can, and bent forward a little to remove some old leaves from a potted geranium. Squashing the leaves in my hand released the distinct aroma with its slightly peppery smell.

'Eew, Mum that's disgusting,' Amy exclaimed, but she wasn't referring to the geranium smell. As I'd leaned forward, a rush of watery substance had shot out of my nose. I cupped my empty hand, and managed to catch most of it before it trickled out through my fingers, and onto the floor.

'What on earth was that?' she said.

'Thank goodness you were standing there next to me. You saw that, didn't you? You're my witness,' I replied. 'That's the liquid I've been telling all the doctors about, and I've never seen a big rush of it like that. If only I'd been able to catch it in a container. There was a little pool of it in my hand, wasn't there?'

'Yes. How revolting. Why is it coming out like that?' said Amy.

'Well, that's exactly what I've been trying to find out. And yet the last doctor, Dr Miller, seems to have completely ignored it, and put me on some stupid pills,' I answered. 'That's it, Amy. It's made up my mind. This can't be right, having fluid pour out of my nose like that, and I'm going to arrange another scan. I'll request it myself this time.'

Unfortunately it wasn't quite as easy as all that to arrange a scan – a doctor's referral was necessary, either from a GP, or a consultant. I certainly didn't anticipate my new consultant cooperating with such a request, so I had to hope a GP would oblige, bearing in mind I was going to be paying for it myself. I knew I would have to be honest about my lack of faith in Dr Miller's judgment, and I went armed with some important correspondence. I had very recently struck up an email relationship with an extremely helpful doctor in India. His name was Dr Anirban Biswas, and he explained to me that his teacher in the relevant area of expertise was a certain Dr Kirtane, in Mumbai. The reason that this was significant was that Dr Kirtane had undertaken the largest series of repairs of CSF leaks (those involving dripping noses) in the world. I couldn't go much higher than that for a second opinion.

Dr Biswas didn't beat about the bush. I showed the GP what he'd written. 'The Betahistine is a hoax and a nuisance at least, in your case. Until a proper diagnosis is carried out about the cause, just trying to give symptomatic relief is unethical medical practice. Seek another opinion from a neuro-otologist who doesn't fight shy of surgery.'

It worked. I got the referral letter I needed, and I proceeded to make arrangements for a new MRI scan. However, I didn't just request a straightforward scan. I asked to have a substance called gadolinium injected through a small needle into a vein in my arm, while I was lying in the scanning tunnel. Was I harbouring masochistic tendencies, I began to wonder? The injection of the contrast agent was my idea; it was because I didn't want to leave anything to chance, even though it meant spending some extra money. The purpose of it was to improve the clarity of the scanned pictures, and make any abnormality more visible to the radiologist.

That worked too – I was on a roll. At last, a scan showing that all was not well in the mastoid bone, the bone through which Mr Ingram had drilled his channel to reach my inner ear. The mastoid bone is normally like a honeycomb, with many air-filled cavities, but my scan report indicated it was full of liquid, with prominent signs of an infection. It prompted a flurry of phone calls and letters over the ensuing week, with a copy of the scan being sent to Mr Ingram, and messages left by anxious GPs for Dr Miller, who seemed to have disappeared. After he'd eventually been tracked down, the male GP who had now taken charge of the matter called me to relay their conversation.

'I've managed to speak to Dr Miller at last. I don't know this consultant – what was your impression of him?' he asked me.

This was a highly unusual question. Whatever doctors thought of each other, they never shared those thoughts with patients. I was tempted to be frank – 'M for misguided, or possibly just downright miserable.'

'I've only had one consultation with him, as you probably know, and he did give me a lot of his time,' I replied. 'However, the end result was not what I expected at all. I really don't think he knows enough about my condition, and he didn't seem prepared to take on board many of the things I was trying to tell him.'

'Hmm, I rather got the feeling his decisions were based around the fact that he is going on holiday soon,' the doctor said. 'He's looked at the scan report, but he still wants you to keep taking the Betahistine. He plans to see you again in August.'

'Yes, August 12 is the appointment date,' I answered. 'But I've been taking the Betahistine for about five weeks now, and it's not doing anything at all to help. I just don't understand why he thinks it will. He's ignored the positive fistula test I had, and now he's ignoring the scan too. By the way, I had a note from my surgeon in Manchester this morning, and his response to the scan was to tell me to talk to Dr Miller about it. They know each other, you see.'

'Would you like me to talk to Dr Miller again tomorrow?' the GP asked. 'I can tell him that you still want a middle ear operation, if that's what you want me to say.'

I was taken aback by the doctor's offer. It was almost as though he was looking for a confrontation with the consultant. I felt slightly nervous about the developing situation, but replied that I *would* like him to have a further conversation.

The same GP called again the next day, just after I'd got in from collecting Amy from school.

'He won't change his mind,' he said. 'I told him everything we'd discussed about your symptoms, and his words were, "there's a difference of opinion." I'm afraid he's not going to see you again.'

I held my breath in astonishment. This was dreadful news. The GP was supposed to be helping me, and now he'd managed to lose me my consultant. 'Oh no, what am I going to do now?' I said, as calmly as I could.

'Dr Miller said he thought it would be best if you were seen by a different specialist,' the GP replied. 'He's going to set up another appointment. He mentioned a name – Mr Sanderson. Does that mean anything to you?'

Did that mean anything to me? I couldn't believe what I was hearing. Mr Sanderson (doctor no.1), Mr Smug to me. Things had now come full circle.

8

SEARCH FOR A BRAIN LEAK

Doctors appeared to be closing ranks around me. It was an unsettling feeling. The content of Dr Kerr's referral letter had been largely ignored, and he was now in retirement. Dr Miller and Mr Ingram were in alliance, having met up at a recent conference, and discussed my case. The former had objected to me questioning his judgment, and dismissed me as his patient, and I was now being referred to a consultant whom I already knew was one of Dr Miller's colleagues. One who, four years ago, had appeared neither thorough, nor particularly caring. The prospect of returning to Mr Sanderson was not one I wished to contemplate.

The famous philosopher Karl Popper had identified a problem such as mine, when he wrote in *The Open Society and Its Enemies*: 'Criticisms by patients is relatively uncommon. Not only are they rarely aware of the relevant facts, but they tend to trust their doctor. They want to keep his goodwill, and may fear that a dispute would sour any subsequent dealings with him, and with other doctors. They may not know how to get a better doctor.' My problem was now exactly that – how to get a better doctor.

I knew London very well. I had lived there for almost twenty years, and attended school there for an additional two, as a teenager. It was, in fact, my school's street address that I decided may hold the solution to my problem – Harley Street, well known for its numerous private doctors' houses, and consulting rooms. The name is synonymous in Britain with some of the best medical expertise. It would mean, yet again, crossing from the NHS back into the private system, to stand a chance of a consultation in the near future, but I could see no alternative. I set about locating a specialist whose credentials seemed to fit my requirements, and then I contacted him by email. I focused on Dr Kerr's summary, my correspondence with Dr Biswas in India, and my most recent scan findings. I was thrilled to find a telephone message from him, as well as an email, in quick reply. Mr Quirke (doctor no.7) was offering to see me.

From the age of fifteen to seventeen, I had joined the daily commuters and travelled by train into London from our family home, twenty-five miles outside the capital. Queen's College, my old school in Harley Street, occupied four elegant, tall houses with Georgian facades, and had first opened in 1848. It became a pioneer in the field of women's education and emancipation, and was the first school in the world to offer academic qualifications to women. I knew at the time I was privileged to be spending the last two years of my schooling there, and to find myself now retracing my steps along the attractive street brought to mind some very happy times. I pushed open the glossy black door to the consulting rooms further down the street from the school, and entered the red brick Victorian building. I was shown into a waiting area that must once have served as a large sitting room. A huge, marble fireplace filled part of the longest wall, large table lamps were perched on antique console tables, and an abundant array of peonies glistened in their crystal vase. There was an air of opulence, and the setting was a distant cry from the dismal, bare strip of a room which I'd come to know well in the Scottish ear, nose and throat clinic. But of course I was paying for the pleasure.

I'd arrived early for my appointment, so I made myself comfortable in one of the upholstered armchairs, and reflected on my childhood for several minutes. How far back did I need to go, I wondered, to detect the first signs of an abnormal head? Had my dance teacher spotted something, when she expressed her view that I may not be destined for stardom as a prima ballerina? 'Heavy on your feet' was the term she'd used, as she dashed my hopes, and clumsy was an adjective that had been regularly directed at me at home. There had been something about my mother's high pitched sneeze that made me wince whenever I heard it – was this an early indication of over sensitive ears? I had always been very susceptible to motion sickness, choosing to sit in the front of the car to alleviate the problem whenever possible, and then of course there was that utterly miserable weekend spent on a luxury yacht, as it cruised across the channel to France and back – miserable not only for me, but for poor Marguerite who had invited me. The use of the yacht, complete with a fully trained crew, was one of my school friend's American father's business perks, but once on board I'd discovered that even the calmest of seas had a disastrous effect on me. So long as the swanky boat was in motion, I was either being sick, or up on deck staring glumly out to sea, sweaty and lethargic, with the stink of exhaust fumes wafting around my head. I couldn't bear to be inside, and Marguerite couldn't bear to be near me. Once we had docked, I miraculously recovered, and wolfed down a large French meal, only for the return journey to be equally wretched. An invitation wasn't extended again.

My childhood reminiscences were interrupted by the calling of my name. Mr Quirke was ready to see me. I went up a flight of stairs, and into another large room. A balding man, handsomely attired in a smart, black suit, stepped forward to greet me. He had piercing, grey eyes, and a lightly freckled complexion. His manner of speaking was terse, and it was clear that he wouldn't take kindly to time wasting. There was something akin to *Alice in Wonderland*'s White Rabbit about him.

'Good afternoon. Please sit down,' he said. 'I'm going to take a look in your ears first of all.'

Without further ado he examined both ears, paying particular attention to the left one, and the scar resulting from my surgery.

'Well, you have a collapsed mastoid, that's clear from looking at it. You must have noticed the deep ditch just behind the ear? You referred in your email to a recent MRI. Do you have the scan report with you? I'd like to see it if I may.'

I rifled around in my bag, the clipped nature of his speech making me flustered. He washed his hands in a small sink in the corner of the room, and then sat down behind his large, mahogany desk. It was almost as though the act of sitting down relaxed him, as he adopted a slower pace, and more genial tone for the next part of our conversation.

'It seems very obvious from this that there is a possible CSF leak somewhere,' he said, waving my folder of papers around. 'It's all here in the scan report. It's probable it was caused by your surgery. You may very well have a perilymph fistula too, bearing in mind the positive test result in Manchester, but you realise that's not going to show up on a scan? I know your surgeon, of course, as he used to be in my team. That was a few years ago.'

Was it my imagination, or was he watching my face for a reaction? A plethora of expletives leapt into my mind, none of which I uttered out loud. Out of all the ENT consultants in the British Isles, I had unknowingly managed to pick my surgeon's ex-boss. What the hell was going to happen now?

'No, I didn't realise that,' I said.

'Yes,' he responded. 'Now, let's be clear – you need to have another operation, there's no doubt about that. But I'm not the person to do it. I'm not prepared to re-open your mastoid bone I'm afraid, because of the delicate surgery you've had. The point is this: If I did the next operation, I wouldn't know exactly what's been done before, and so I'd run the risk of damaging the superior semicircular canal. I'm not having you sue me for causing you a dead ear. I'm happy to send a letter about it though. Whatever's going on here, it's related to your proce-dure last year.'

He didn't wait for my approval. Before I could ask when he intended to write the letter, he had opened a drawer in the desk, taken out a dictaphone, and started talking into it. I was aware I was starting to gawp, and closed my mouth tightly shut.

'I am writing to let you know that I have seen this lady for a further consultation, concerning her left ear. You will remember her clearly,' his letter began. 'Personally, I feel that any further surgery should be done by your good self,' it concluded, and he snapped off the dictaphone.

'I'll get a copy sent out to Dr Miller, and your GP as well, once the letter's been typed up,' he said. He leaned back in his chair, evidently satisfied with the decisive way he was drawing the consultation to a close. Q for quick.

'Thank you very much, Mr Quirke, that's extremely help-ful,' I said.

I gathered up my belongings piled in a heap by the chair, and stood up to shake his hand. The doctor smiled, and gave my hand a firm shake.

I skipped down the stairs, and out onto Harley Street. Things could hardly have gone better. Mr Ingram could surely not ignore that letter, coming as it did from his ex-boss, and Mr Quirke hadn't been in any doubt that action needed to be taken. He had put his opinion clearly in writing so, if Mr Ingram were to drag his heels or be unhappy about interference from the senior consultant I would have no qualms about asking my GP to step in. I had recently read something that astonished and worried me in equal part. A perilymph fistula was appar-ently a 'controversial condition', one that not all ear specialists recognised. Dr Jeremy Hornibrook, in New Zealand, writing a detailed paper on the subject in 2012, put it this way: 'It became an almost emotional issue in Otolaryngology, with believers and non believers.' Mr Quirke, it seemed, was a believer, so I definitely needed to keep him as my ally.

I was becoming adept at finding cheap places to stop over for the night, as I travelled hither and thither on my health quest, and I set off on my walk to the next one. It was in a less salubrious part of town.

It didn't take long for Mr Quirke's intervention to bear fruit. His letters had left Harley Street on June 20, and ten days later I was making my way back through the scruffy entrance area to the Manchester hospital, bypassing the straggled group of outdoor smokers in their hospital gowns. I had been summoned to see Mr Ingram. There had also been a change of plan that very morning, as I'd received a call requesting that I make arrangements to spend the night in hospital. I was going to be undergoing a procedure called CT cisternography. I didn't need to have this explained, as I already knew it was a means of identifying whether a patient was suffering from a CSF leak. The troubling aspect was that it involved a lumbar puncture (often referred to as a spinal tap) and I, like anyone else confronted with this unappealing form of examination, wasn't relishing the prospect of having a long needle poked into my backbone.

First I had to come face to face with Mr Ingram again, after more than seven months apart, and the idea seemed only a fraction less unappealing. I sat waiting on my hospital bed, in the same ward where I had been recuperating, unsuccessfully, after the surgery. I looked up each time I heard the ward door opening, and at last the surgeon appeared. He gingerly approached the side of my bed, with a concerned look in his eyes. I took it upon myself to try and break the ice, and smooth over any ill feelings that we may have towards each other.

'Hello. How are you? It feels strange being back on this ward again,' I said. 'Obviously you've been in touch with Mr Quirke – I hope you understand why I went to see him? Things weren't working out very well with Dr Miller.'

'Yes, I realise you wanted to get a second opinion, and I understand that,' he replied.

'I know I'm being kept in for the night. Is that because I have to rest after the procedure?' I asked.

'It's for a number of reasons. We're going to be doing a comprehensive round of scans, both CT and MRI, this afternoon and I've no way of knowing when the process will be finished. The radiography department are being very helpful, and slotting you in amongst their scheduled work. CT cisternography also involves a lumbar puncture, and yes, you do need to lie down for several hours after that. I'll be seeing you before my clinic starts after lunch tomorrow, and I'll make sure I've studied the scans myself before I talk to you. Please be there about one forty five. The clinic starts at two.'

'Yes, of course. So I won't see you until tomorrow?' I said.

'That's correct,' he answered.

His eyes had regained a slight sparkle now, and his face had softened.

'See you tomorrow,' he said. We were parting on friendly terms. I felt confident that he had made arrangements for a thorough investigation to be undertaken, and that I was in the right place at last.

I pulled the curtain around the bed, and changed into my blue hospital gown. Half an hour later a porter arrived with a chair, in which he wheeled me down to the radiography section. I was introduced to Dr Shetty, a friendly doctor who was weeks away from becoming a consultant radiologist. Mr Ingram had told me on the ward that she had a special interest in SCDS.

'Hello. Is it alright if I address you as Philippa?' she said.

'Yes of course. That's fine.'

'Well, Philippa, it would be very helpful for me if you could quickly run through your current symptoms. We can't take you through for the scanning just yet as an emergency has come in, and obviously that patient has to be treated first. There may be a bit of a wait I'm afraid.'

'Yes, ok. The primary symptom at the moment is the fluid that builds up,' I began. 'I'm not sure that Mr Ingram fully appreciates the quantity of it. I was woken this morning at four o'clock, and I had to drain out the area around my left ear, by suctioning all the liquid down my throat, little by little. This takes quite a long time. Once I was up and about, it was just flowing freely down again, and the pressure and pain immediately built up once more in the ear, and the mastoid region. Painkillers do virtually nothing to help with this. A headache develops all around the back of my head, and it only eases when I lie down. I have to be in a lying position, or tilt my head far back at an angle, to get this watery liquid in the right position to then suction it away. The whole bizarre process carries on relentlessly throughout the day. It's at its very worst in the evening, maybe that's because I'm so exhausted by then?'

Dr Shetty looked at me closely, bafflement etched on her face.

'Of course, as Mr Ingram knows,' I continued, 'I've had some of this clear, watery substance dripping out of my nose, and even a sudden rush of it on one occasion. I have a sensation of fullness in the ear almost all the time, and sometimes the bone behind my ear is very painful, and feels inflamed inside. I have lots of nausea, lots of unsteadiness, but the vertigo I was experiencing seems to have lessened at last. Thank goodness.'

Dr Shetty opened her mouth to speak, but a further thought of mine jumped out, 'Oh, I nearly forgot, I particularly wanted to tell you about my left hand, and upper arm. I'm frequently getting sharp pain or throbbing, sometimes tingling too, in those areas. It's most noticeable in my thumb and forefinger. They're badly affected.'

'I see,' said the doctor, nodding. She leaned forward to touch me lightly on the shoulder. 'I can tell you've been having a difficult time, and I know you've travelled down from Scotland. That's a long way to have to come. We're going to do our best to find out what's wrong, and see if we can help you. The thumb and forefinger pain is interesting – those two fingers are connected to a particular nerve, so I'll do a specific scan of your neck to take a look at that.'

Her compassion touched me, and I could feel my emotion rising to the surface, looking for a release. I didn't want to start crying, so I swallowed hard, and forced a slight smile.

I sat waiting for over an hour. All my belongings had been left up on the ward, and in nothing but a flimsy gown and some slippers, I started to feel the cold. I was relieved when Dr Shetty eventually reappeared, and said they were ready for me. If I'd known the endurance test that lay ahead of me, I would have realised exactly how misplaced that relief was. CT cisternography basically consists of a CT scan to start with, then the lumbar puncture procedure (during which a contrast dye is administered), and a second CT scan immediately after that. The two sets of scanned images are subsequently compared, so that the radiographers can look for any signs of escaping cerebrospinal fluid. In my case, Dr Shetty was doing an additional CT scan to look for an explanation of the hand problem, and also an MRI scan – presumably just to make sure all bases had been covered. A marathon scanning session beckoned.

After the initial spell in the scanner, I was transferred to a different room, and asked to lie on a radiographic table. Suspended over it was a television-like monitor. An x-ray beam was going to create a sequence of pictures, and these would be projected onto the fluorescent screen as video images, to be used to watch and guide the progress of the procedure. I was told I could look at the screen, but it was imperative I kept perfectly still. The table was then tilted slightly, so that my body was at the precise angle necessary. There was an atmosphere of hard concentration, and professional efficiency, among the staff around the table. Everyone, including me, knew there was no margin for error. I felt the chill from my lower spine being numbed with anaesthetic, and I imagined the enormous needle being prepared for insertion between two lumbar bones (vertebrae). I averted my eyes from the screen – it was one thing to know that a sample of CSF would be removed from my spinal canal, and a dye injected to replace it; it was another thing entirely to watch it happening. I felt a dull pain as the needle was pulled out. It had gone in almost without me noticing it. The staff relaxed, and resumed their chit-chat.

I had to be whisked back into the scanning machine and, by the time I was being installed into the MRI tunnel for the final radiographic stint, I feared I might not be able to stay the course. Hours had passed since I'd left my bed on the ward. I hadn't eaten or drunk anything, I was starting to shiver, my lower back now felt sore and tender, and I was developing an awful headache. The amount of willpower required to brave the tunnel challenge, and stick it out without buzzing for release, was colossal. I had to urge myself through every minute – reminding myself of everything I'd achieved to get to this point, cursing the turn of events that had made it all necessary, and vowing that I would complete the scan, and hear Mr Ingram telling me he'd found the problem, and would put everything right again. The radiographer helped. By anyone's standards, I wasn't having an easy time, and by praising my fortitude, and sending encouraging messages through the speaker, he gave me the resolve I needed to get to the end. As he helped me out, I thanked him for the support.

After ten minutes of sitting in my chair in the now empty waiting area, Dr Shetty re-emerged. She looked weary but gratified.

'Hello, Philippa. Are you ok? I know we've kept you down here a very long time.'

I looked up at the clock on the wall, and saw it was nearly eight. I wondered whether Dr Shetty normally stayed so late in the evening.

'I've been working my way through all the images from the scanning,' she said, 'and if you come with me now I could show them to you, while they're still up on the screens.'

I agreed, and followed her into a room where a long row of computers was arranged on a work bench against the wall. We sat down in front of one of them, and Dr Shetty began explaining what was being shown. There was my head unfolding in all its glory, as she opened up the cross-sectional pictures, and examined the bones and tissues from all directions, enlarging and shrinking parts at will by the click of her mouse. The experience was surreal. Exhausted from the trials of the afternoon, barely able to think straight, and only half dressed, I was sitting alone in an empty hospital department, with a woman I'd met just a few hours ago, miles from home, staring at picture after picture of my own magnified head.

'So you see, there really is no evidence of any leak,' she said, 'and that's extremely good news.'

I turned to look at her. Was she being serious? Good news? Before I could put this into words, she continued.

'As I'm sure you'll understand, a CSF leak is a very grave matter, so it can only be a good thing that we can't find any sign of one. I really don't think there's any doubt about that. As you can see, we have done very extensive investigations. There is, however, what appears to be a severe problem in your mastoid on the left side – the bone through which Mr Ingram approached your semicircular canal.'

She zoomed in on the relevant section on one of the scans, and pointed to the area in question.

'There seems to be a chronic inflammatory process here, and I wouldn't be surprised if Mr Ingram advises a total mastoidectomy, in other words for that whole area to be completely removed. Obviously he'll discuss that with you himself, when he sees you tomorrow.'

I let out a lengthy sigh of relief. A problem had been pinpointed. It may not have been quite what I thought it would be, but I couldn't have asked for a more dedicated doctor to do the investigation. She must be right. I could retire to my bed, safe in the knowledge that a plan would be sorted out once a new day had arrived.

'Thank you so much for all your help, Dr Shetty,' I replied. 'You've been very kind indeed, and I'm really sorry you've had to stay so late to do all this. Shouldn't you be going home now?'

She laughed. 'Yes, I definitely should. My husband isn't going to be pleased, as I promised I wouldn't be late again this evening. He'll be putting the children to bed. I'll call for a porter to come and take you back up to the ward.'

My night was spent tossing and turning in my uncomfortable bed. My head and body ached all over, my mind was racing with thoughts of needles and scanners, and my next door bed neighbour added to the discomfort by snoring loudly throughout the night. Her adenoids had been removed. I contemplated hurling a slipper to shut her up. The next day could only be an improvement on the one I was leaving behind.

9

I WAS STUPEFIED

The rattle of the tea trolley signalled the start of the morning on the ward.

Having hardly slept a wink, I hauled myself up, and washed and dressed. Apart from Mr Ingram's reference the previous day to lying down for a few hours, no-one had given me any guidance about limiting the after effects of a lumbar puncture. My head, neck, and back were now crying out for pain relief. I took a couple of analgesic tablets out of my bag, and swallowed them with a large mouthful of tea. I hoped the pain would ease as the day progressed. When I was halfway through my breakfast bowl of cornflakes, one of the nurses approached to tell me I would soon be taken downstairs again. One of the scans from the previous day needed to be re-done. I'd been wondering how I was going to fill the morning, but yet another scan hadn't been considered. I decided I should think positively, and just be impressed by the hospital's thoroughness – Dr Shetty must have noticed something important that had been overlooked, when viewing the scans with fresh eyes.

Another long wait on a hard chair ensued, before the relatively pain free, horizontal stretch in the CT scanner. I was ready and waiting in the clinic area well before the allotted meeting time, having collected my belongings from the ward, and been handed my discharge paperwork. As the clock hand ticked its way closer to the twelve, the room had been steadily filling up with patients arriving to see the team of ENT doctors, but there was still no sign of Mr Ingram. The pain in my head and neck wasn't dispersing; on the contrary, the build up of pressure was constant, and I was now in extreme discomfort. I'd purchased a large bottle of water from the hospital shop, and kept taking regular glugs, wishing it would lessen the agony.

Mr Ingram scuttled past me, his registrar in tow, and they disappeared into the consulting room a few yards away, closing the door. It was now after two o'clock, and I knew the consultant should be seeing his first clinic patient. I felt tense. Tense from the pain I was battling with, and frustrated at the lack of time that had been allowed for our conversation.

The registrar emerged from the consulting room, and called my name.

Mr Ingram was sitting at a desk at the far end of the room when I entered. He didn't stand up to greet me. His face was expressionless. The registrar closed the door behind me, and remained standing near it, out of my sight. I took the seat across from the surgeon and waited, anticipating an enquiry after my health.

'I've been through all the scans and, as you know from Dr Shetty, there's no evidence of a CSF leak,' the surgeon began. 'We are ninety-eight percent sure of that. I'm afraid it's impossible to be one hundred percent certain, but a very thorough search has been undertaken.'

I nodded, and maintained eye contact. I was waiting for him to expand on the problem that *had* been identified, but his stiff demeanour and unsmiling appearance was giving me a very bad feeling. Rather than a caring consultant discussing a patient's circumstances, the atmosphere in the room suggested a headmaster displeased with a wayward pupil. Thud, thud, thud, my heart was beating loud in my ear.

'The pain that you're apparently getting in your left hand seems to have been caused by nerve damage during the surgery,' he continued. 'Unfortunately there's nothing that can be done about that. It would be far too dangerous to try to rectify it.'

'I see,' I replied. 'But Dr Shetty explained to me last night that you will probably need to re-operate, because of all the fluid in the mastoid.'

'There isn't any fluid.' He looked straight at me, unblinking. Thud, thud, thud, the volume of the heartbeat went up a notch.

'There isn't anything wrong with the mastoid,' he reiterated. An explanation for the way his colleague had interpreted the scans wasn't forthcoming, and it was plain that all investigations were now terminated. There was little attempt to conceal a wish to round up the conversation, as the surgeon glanced up at the registrar, indicating as much.

I was stupefied. There was a small window directly behind Mr Ingram, and for a brief moment I felt an overwhelming desire to tip his chair up, and toss him through it. Fortunately for the doctor I've never been a violent person. If only he could show some emotion, express empathy, offer some guidance about what to do next. It wasn't what he was saying that exasperated me. It was how he was presenting it to me. I felt so let down. I needed him to understand how devastating this was for me, to help me counteract the fear of never being able to function normally again. Norman Cousins, in his book *Anatomy of an Illness*, explained how his doctor encouraged him 'to believe I was a respected partner with him in the total undertaking', and how important that was in the process of getting well again. I didn't feel a partner, let alone a respected one; I felt like an interfering nuisance.

The shock from the cold facts being imparted was temporarily numbing the pain that had been shooting up and down my neck and back, but I still couldn't find the cognitive abilities I needed, to organise all the questions flying around inside my head. I grasped at one of them.

'But what about the fistula test that Kate carried out last year? Why was it positive?'

'There doesn't seem to be an explanation for that,' the surgeon answered. 'Your hearing tests don't indicate that you have a perilymph fistula, and the large amount of fluid you've described doesn't fit in with that either. I'll summarise everything in a letter to your GP. Perhaps you should get your salivary glands looked at.'

With that, he stood up from his chair, and looked at the registrar again. The door was duly opened, and they both stared at me, counting on my exit. I knew the hearing test comment simply wasn't true, but what was the point in trying to argue it out? I'd read about many cases where normal hearing, or varying types of hearing loss, had been found with the ear fistula, but I was also aware I'd be wasting my time disputing the facts with an experienced specialist, particularly knowing as I did now that it was considered a controversial condition. I didn't have the strength to put up a fight. The two doctors wanted to get on with their clinic, and I had become a hindrance to that. I needed to be removed.

'If anything else occurs to you in the meantime, could you please add it to the letter you're sending to my GP?' I added feebly, as I was leaving. He nodded.

Finding my way out of the hospital, back to the train station, buying the ticket, it was all a blur. I had pinned all my hopes on Mr Ingram establishing what needed to be fixed, and reinstating me as his patient, and those hopes had come to nothing. I was now without a consultant, and without a plan for what to do next. Severe nausea had set in, from the intense level the pain had reached, my head was at bursting point and I had hours of train travel to contend with. For the time being, it was vital to blank out what had happened in the hospital, as I was in no fit state to handle the crushing disappointment.

I focused all my efforts on getting home, where I longed to be, lying in a comfortable bed. It dawned on me that my car had been left at Dunbar station, at best a twenty-minute drive from my house, but to get to it I had to change trains. Even if I somehow managed to endure two train journeys, how was I going to be able to drive home in the dark, with excruciating pain up and down my spine, and throughout my head? I would have gladly re-enacted the two long and complex deliveries of my children, if it could be done in exchange for the gruesome pain I was now suffering. I'd recently been reading about Dr Brand, an English orthopaedic surgeon, who worked extensively with lepers in India. He'd established that the lepers' desensitised nerve endings put them at increased risk of injury in various ways, because there was the lack of a pain mechanism. Pain acts as a warning system, and the individual can mobilise their response to its signals. The question in my mind, as I sat on the train, was what on earth should be my response to this pain, the like of which I'd never experienced?

I was on a stopping train, filling up with people at every station along its route, and an overweight man chose to spread himself out in the cramped space next to my window seat. He took a toasted sandwich out of his canvas holdall, and took off the greasy wrapper. The smell hit me with a punch. Panic, breathlessness, nausea, claustrophobia, pressure, dizziness – they gathered themselves up into a giant bomb, and swooped down to envelope me. I jumped up from my seat, grabbed my bag and coat, and entreated the passenger to let me out into the aisle. The alternative would have been to vomit right there in my seat, as he ate his snack.

I escaped to the standing area outside the carriage entrance door, and had to think rapidly as the train was now slowly approaching the destination where I should disembark to change trains. I couldn't see a means of getting home safely, alone in such a state of agony. I made the rash decision to remain on the train to Edinburgh, rather than alighting to follow my originally intended route. If I kept my distance from the other passengers, and found a quiet corner to stretch out my body on the floor, I would just have to hang on. Once in the capital, I would take a taxi from the station to the hospital A&E department, to seek help.

'I think it could be as high as about forty percent, the number of people that get a spinal headache after a lumbar puncture,' the doctor at the Edinburgh Royal Infirmary Hospital told me. 'Have you been drinking plenty of water to re-hydrate your system?'

I confirmed that I had, thinking as I replied that no-one in Manchester had advised me to do that. Nor had they said a word about the possibility of a spinal headache. And this wasn't just any old headache. Heavens no. This was what might be described as the epitome of physical discomfort. It had been patently clear to the hospital staff that I'd been there on my own – had anyone given a second thought to how I was going to get back to Scotland?

'Did you say it had been done in Manchester? It seems surprising they allowed you to travel all that way on a train, straight after the procedure,' the doctor added, echoing my thoughts. 'I'll be back shortly – I'm just going to take a look at your medical records on the computer.'

I was lying flat on the hospital trolley, in a busy emergency room. Just raising my head an inch to talk had felt as though my brain was being squeezed down through my neck. It was now obvious to me that the extended period sitting upright on the train, and earlier on the hospital chairs, had reduced me to this wreckage. From my horizontal vantage point I watched the doctor, with a huddle of students around him, studying the computer screen, and then looking across to my trolley. I heard the all too familiar words 'panic attack' being whispered among them. It was the same emergency department that had dealt with me in a panic-stricken condition two weeks after my surgery, and the record of that occasion eight months ago had no doubt shown up on the screen.

Once the pain had subsided to a manageable level, a kindly nurse took pity on me, offering to ring around in an effort to find a local taxi that would collect me from the hospital, and deliver me home. It was now after midnight, and the journey would take about three quarters of an hour. Once in the black cab I had to persuade the driver to stop at an automated cash machine before we left the city, otherwise I wasn't going to be able to pay him the substantial fare my trip would cost. It was one o'clock in the morning when I crept into our quiet house. I could hear the faint bleeps of the dialysis machine at work where Hugh was sleeping, or trying to. I looked in on Patrick who was deep in slumber, and made my way to bed in the spare room upstairs. Seeing my son always hardened my resolve.

To say it had not been the day I'd been hoping for would be an understatement of inordinate proportions. It took a further four days of resting flat before my usual daily activities could be resumed. I vowed never in my life to inflict a lumbar puncture on my body again. Sadly, some vows have to be broken.

10

A SORRY STATE OF AFFAIRS

There's no getting away from the fact that dizzy patients are complex patients.

It takes time and effort to evaluate vestibular disorders properly, and then treat them effectively. Now that its workings are much better understood, neuroscientists marvel at the sophistication and sensitivity of the vestibular system, whose most important task is to keep track of where the head is. Dr Daniel Merfeld, director of Jenks Vestibular Physiology Laboratory, at Massachusetts Eye and Ear Infirmary, explained in an interview the act of walking, a process most of us humans take for granted: 'We are unconsciously juggling six inverted pendulums, six mechanically independent units with masses above the pivot point – a feat that amounts to balancing six pencils on your palm simultaneously. Bipedalism is largely a top-down operation overseen by the vestibular system, which gauges the head position relative to the floor, and signals the brain to adjust the pivot points accordingly.' That is certainly something to marvel at.

And then there's the 'hardware' of the vestibular system to consider. It's small and transparent, and can be awkward to locate. Dr Merfeld described it thus: 'It's basically a cavity in the skull, filled with fluid, and lined with membranes. It's almost the absence of something, rather than the presence.'

Unfortunately, there's no shortage of dizzy patients. The Vestibular Disorders Association (VEDA) has recently estimated that in America alone as many as thirty-five percent of people aged forty and above (approximately sixty-nine million Americans) have experienced some form of vestibular dysfunction. From a broader perspective, looking at ENT matters in general, a study undertaken in 2012 estimated that the ENT caseload for British GPs amounted to up to a quarter of adult, and half of paediatric, consultations. And yet, despite concerns over a thirty-year period, the study revealed that little improvement had been made in the provision of undergraduate ENT teaching. A compulsory ENT placement was only available to about half of the students, and the majority of ENT consultants questioned did not consider newly qualified doctors to be proficient in managing even the common ENT problems.

BPPV (benign paroxysmal positional vertigo), discussed earlier in the book, is a good case in point. It is in fact the most common cause of vertigo and can affect adults of any age, especially older ones – children too, but less frequently. It is triggered by certain head positions and movements, and most cases occur for no obvious reason; a person may just be getting out of bed in the morning and finds the room has started to spin. Despite being so common, BPPV is missed by many doctors, both GPs and ENT specialists alike. Sometimes this is actually down to the Dix-Hallpike test, used to identify the condition by looking for involuntary eye movements (nystagmus). The test is not foolproof, partly because of the fatigable property of nystagmus. Instead of just dismissing all those with normal tests, suspect patients should be brought back and re-tested by the doctors, preferably the next morning.

A similar situation prevails in the United States, where ENT training is not routinely covered in medical school either. Unless they actively pursue it, the majority of doctors there have no formal exposure to that aspect of training. When it comes to vestibular education, things are worse – it is very poor indeed, even within the most highly-regarded programmes. The CBC News journalist Meredith Levine, when examining the situation in Canada, discovered 'a pronounced shortage of inner ear specialists.' Patients who on average spent 'two years bouncing around the health-care system' before finding David Pothier, an inner ear specialist within Toronto University, were the lucky ones – 'most vestibular patients don't end up under the care of a neurologist.'

Seen in the context of this sorry state of affairs, it became easier to understand why it had taken nearly four years for me to get an SCDS diagnosis, and why despite the involvement of seven ENT consultants (to this point) there had still been no satisfactory resolution. Throughout the whole period, I'd never been offered extensive vestibular and auditory testing, which all vertigo patients require, nor had sufficient time ever been allocated to the detailed taking of my history, or a very thorough physical examination. As a rough estimate, fifteen percent of chronically dizzy people are likely to be people symptomatic from SCDS – little wonder that many of those may be undiagnosed, or misdiagnosed.

After my return from Manchester, I was faced with a stark choice: either abandon my search for answers and live for the rest of my life with a set of symptoms that were worse than those before my operation, or I do what Mr Ingram had suggested, and rule out any problem with the salivary glands. Without doing the latter, I suspected I was never going to find another ENT consultant that would be bold enough to review my case.

The new stage of my health odyssey began towards the end of July, at a consultation with Professor Lello (doctor no.8), yet another specialist that I had had to locate myself. He was a be-spectacled gentleman with a friendly, open face, and a full head of whitish grey hair. From our first exchange his thoroughness and courtesy was impressive, and not a trace of arrogance had attached itself to this doctor, despite his distinguished career in a number of countries, and the many positions he had held within professional associations. It was a tremendous relief to find he was on my side from the outset, and was happy to plot a clear path for seeing whether salivary gland trouble could be eliminated. Here was someone who really listened, and inspired me with confidence. L for level headed. The first examination arranged by the professor, an ultrasound, showed nothing unusual, so the next step was a sialogram, a detailed x-ray of the salivary ducts and glands.

At the rate I was going, there would soon cease to be a part of my body that hadn't had the indignity of having dye injected into it. On this occasion it was to be through minuscule ducts of the salivary glands inside my left cheek, and under my bottom lip but, as I lay on the x-ray table keeping as still as a stone, I realised that the elderly radiologist looming over me had a substantial obstacle in his path – an incredibly shaky hand. Over the course of several attempts, the hand, which was holding the tiny needle that had to be inserted into the ducts, hovered around my face, and then wobbled its way inside my wide open mouth, only to exit again some minutes later. By the fifth shaky attempt, and with an aching jaw, I was having trouble controlling a giggle, as suppressed laughter is always the most devilish. I would be making the poor man's Herculean task even harder, if my body were to start wriggling around as well. I took some deep breaths, thought some miserable thoughts to dispel the sniggers, and willed him to succeed before I ruined everything by spluttering. Success, the needle was in, and the dye was filling up the gland. I could see the radiologist's hunched shoulders relax.

'It's a very small duct that the needle has to go into, but I don't recall ever having had so much trouble,' he said. 'I was intending to put the dye into one of the other ducts as well, but as that took so long I think we'll just go with what we've got.'

I couldn't answer because of the risk of undoing his handiwork, so I gently moved my head up and down to show my acceptance. The whole process with the x-rays was supposed to have taken about half an hour, and I'd already been lying on the table for considerably longer than that. When we looked at the x-ray images together a little later, it was fascinating to see all the squiggly rivulets running under my skin, but impossible for me to know whether there was anything untoward about them. The radiologist assured me there wasn't.

Despite an all clear on the working of the glands, and a careful study of my Manchester scans releasing nothing new, Professor Lello wasn't prepared to leave any stone unturned, and requested that I let one of his colleagues give me the once-over. As he specifically wanted a branchial cleft cyst to be ruled out, I thought I'd better do my homework to identify what they were looking for: a type of birth defect, resulting from a failure of obliteration of one of the branchial clefts in the neck. In fish, these develop into gills – a good thing I hadn't mentioned to Professor Lello my webbed toes, two on each foot. Perhaps my holey head had been enough to make him suspicious of further weirdness – this time, a fluid filled pocket, in a lump of abnormally formed tissues.

It was Mr Pickering (doctor no.9) who was charged with this task. Finding nothing after an examination of my mouth, and a good deal of manipulation of my neck and jaw, he took it upon himself to offer me his words of wisdom.

'Every doctor wants to be able to help a patient. However, maybe I'm the one who needs to tell you it's now time for us to think about just helping you learn to manage your symptoms.' P for patronising. What on earth did the man think I'd been doing for the past five years and more?

Professor Lello readily accepted we had now gone full circle, and he put it in writing in a thoughtful letter: 'I agree with you, and Dr Kerr, that investigations should centre on the ear and mastoid area. Common things being common, it would be remiss if the previous surgery in the region of the left ear was not carefully reviewed, in terms of being the possible cause of your current problems.' This was all well and good, but I now had to find another ENT consultant, and I had been fast using up the available supply.

Shortly before the letter arrived, my family and I attended my nephew's wedding in Suffolk, nearly four hundred miles south from where we lived. It was seeing me in person over several days, managing the symptoms that Mr Pickering thought I needed to be taught how to manage, and gaining some comprehension of how badly my condition restricted everyday life, which brought it home to my eldest sister (my nephew's mother) what I was up against. Corresponding, or talking on the phone, wasn't a substitute for seeing something firsthand. From this point on, she started to become more closely involved in how I was faring.

A balance disorder is an invisible condition. Unless you're being physically sick as a result of it, or literally falling over or unable to stand, there are no outward signs of how incredibly unwell it is making you feel, and that makes the job of dealing with it even harder, and the need for understanding from others even greater. Add to the mix, reluctance to be thought a complainer, and a wish not to burden one's family with anxiety, and it becomes an extremely isolating experience.

The support I received from my friends and family was invaluable – I couldn't have kept going without it. But depending on how I was coping each day, it could bring a torrent of conflicting reactions. I wanted support but not pity, correspondence but not interrogation, contact but not regular news of wonderful holidays, and 'normal' lives others were enjoying. I didn't let on how hard I was to please. It's only when you're in a period of serious and protracted ill health that all these feelings come to light. Many of the emails I received, enquiring how I was, were both reassuring and exhausting. They usually required answering, and the answers frequently produced more questions. I was the one desperately seeking answers, and the questions from others took up energy and time, both of which were in short supply. The messages I most welcomed were those offering help of a specific nature, and the times I needed the contact above all others was not (contrary to what many thought) when a scan, or a test, or a surgery was happening, but all the gaps in between – the interminable periods when I was in danger of losing hope, and needed ways to stay positive. It's little comfort to be told that you're doing a great job of battling your illness, as though it's a character test, and you have passed it. But what I was learning most of all throughout this period was what fantastic and loyal friends I had, and how all of them, each in their different way, were letting me know they cared about me. That was the most helpful thing of all.

I decided to try a new tack to find myself the next ENT consultant. I had been back in touch with Kate, the Manchester audiologist, about the negative pressure that she had recorded in my ear after the operation, and with that in mind I organised a free hearing test at House of Hearing, in Edinburgh. The audiologist there proved very helpful, and at the end of the session suggested a local doctor that he felt he could recommend. And so it came about that, in September 2008, I met Mr Scott (doctor no.10).

The most noticeable characteristic of this middle-aged doctor was his Irish accent. He had an easy and fluent way of conversing, a natural charm. The consultation began very positively, Mr Scott assuring me that he would examine my most up-to-date scans and that by carefully retracing the steps of everything that had occurred, he should be able to throw some light on my dilemma. He seemed relaxed and cheerful. He examined my ears, and then decided he wanted to take a closer look at things, by means of an endoscopy – the same uncomfortable probing that Mr Wood (doctor no.2) had undertaken all those months ago. Looking into my nose to spray the anaesthetic, he suddenly bounced backwards, squealing with surprise.

'Goodness. How extraordinary,' he said.

He peered at me, stuck a lump of cotton wool up the nostril that had just given him the fright, and shot out of the room, muttering that he wouldn't be long.

I was left on my own, perched on a chair, wondering what peculiarity had been unearthed this time. Out of all my medical encounters, this one had to be the most bizarre. As the minutes passed, I concluded that perhaps the finding of something was in itself a step forward, as I'd come to dread all reports of nothing showing up.

Mr Scott flounced back into the room, still looking flustered and rather over-excited.

'I'm sorry about that,' he said. 'I just needed to get something, and while I was out there I decided to have a word with one of my colleagues about what had caught my eye. I don't think I've seen one of those for about twenty years. I was checking it couldn't be relevant to your current problems.'

He didn't elaborate, so I asked the obvious questions: 'What is it that you saw? What's so unusual – have you found something wrong with me?'

He chuckled. 'It's called a Jacobson's organ,' he said. 'It's a sort of throwback to Prehistoric man.'

Oh terrific, I thought, more evidence that I'm very imperfectly formed. When a cat comes across an interesting smell, holding its mouth open, with the lips curled back and the teeth showing, it's known as the flehmen response, and will almost certainly be happening as the result of a prompt from this sensitive, odour-detecting organ. It's found in all snakes, lizards and many mammals, but scientists still debate over how frequently it can be identified in adult humans and, more precisely, whether it has any functionality for them, in the way it does for the animals.

'It's just a little pit, about two centimetres inside your right nostril,' said the consultant, 'and I've never seen one so clearly defined as yours. I really don't think it has any relevance though. We'll carry on with the examination now.'

Prehistoric woman tipped her head back, knowing what to expect.

'I'd like you to try suctioning away some of the fluid in the way you've described,' he added, once the endoscope was painfully trawling around.

In this uncomfortable position, with the metal instrument deep within my nasal passages, I was not going to attempt talking, to explain to the doctor this would not normally be how I would go about it. I just had to give it my best shot and, needless to say, the doctor told me he couldn't see anything.

Mr Scott sat down behind his desk again. We talked a little further about my symptoms, and then he pulled some of the scans out of a large, brown envelope. Within seconds, it was clear that these were out-of-date scans he was holding, and I pointed that out to him. I trusted Professor Lello, who had informed me he'd made a special trip to deposit the correct images with Mr Scott in time for our meeting, so I began to feel a little uneasy about this doctor's blasé manner. I sensed that he didn't know quite what to do with me. Perhaps I should have seen what was coming.

'Well, you've been here for about forty-five minutes,' he said, looking down at his watch, and then back at me with a smile. 'You seem to have coped with that alright. There can't be too much wrong with you, can there?' S for sarcastic.

I was literally winded. I could not believe what he was saying to me. He had deliberately coaxed me to have confidence in him, to share all the information, to trust him. Then he had knocked me back – with a smile. Tears of shock dribbled down my face.

Seeing me crying, he rapidly tried to recover the situation.

'I was at a wedding at the weekend, and I surprised myself as I got a bit emotional there too,' he said. 'It's ok, I understand.'

Was I dealing with a simpleton? Didn't he even realise he had caused the tears? What had my health got to do with a wedding? I was lost for words, furious and desperate in equal measure. I couldn't bear to be in the room with him any longer, and stood up to leave.

'It may seem like a retrograde step, but I think we should consider trying another grommet in your ear,' said Mr Scott. 'Have a think about that, and we can liaise by email. I'm going to be away in America for a few weeks, but I'll be checking my messages.'

I said I'd think about it, and would let him know. I quickly headed out of the building, keeping my blotchy face staring down at the ground, and walked along to my car. I flung my things onto the passenger seat, and slammed my hand down hard on the steering wheel. If I never saw another doctor again, it would still be too soon.

11

BAROMETER HEAD

To be honest, there hadn't been many opportunities for putting my Greek literature in translation exam success to good use. But the time had arrived. When it comes to dealing with anger, Aristotle's the man: 'One who is angry at the right things and with the right people, and furthermore, as he ought, when he ought, and as long as he ought, is praised. The good-tempered man tends to be unperturbed, and not to be led by passion, but to be angry in the manner, at the things, and for the length of time, that the rule dictates.' (The Nicomachean Ethics, Book IV)

Of course he was correct – channelled in the right way, anger could be a very productive force. Mr Scott had certainly made me angry, and I had to use that emotion, and achieve something with it.

There had been no further rush of liquid out of my head, since the incident with my daughter earlier in the year, but the fluid was there all the time, day and night, continuing to build up with relentless regularity. I had become a liquid version of the traditional egg timer. Turn me upside down, and I'd suction the fluid out, trickle by trickle; turn me up the right way again, and my head would slowly fill up once more. The big problem was that the doctors couldn't see what was happening and, in the light of Mr Scott's remarks, I began to wonder whether they even believed it was happening. Did they actually think it was all in my imagination or, even worse, some attention-seeking scheme that I'd dreamt up? The very thought infuriated me, and it pushed me to prove them wrong.

While doing his internal examination, Mr Scott had confirmed he could see the little tube from the middle ear to the throat moving around, while I tried to follow his instruction to suction out fluid. The fact that he'd seen this, confirmed what I'd suspected – I must be drawing it out, drop by drop, down into the back of my throat.

I sent an email to the doctor, who was now in America.

'My reason for contacting you is that I have found a way to collect the fluid. The fact that you could see the Eustachian tube moving, spurred me on to experiment with other positions for doing my suctioning, and yesterday I recorded the collection details.'

I spared him the blow-by-blow account of lying on the sofa, tipping myself upside down while trying to avoid triggering a vertigo attack, using the little muscles at the back of my throat to pull every drop of liquid I could into my mouth, then spitting it out, little by little, into a bowl. I did however give him the times, and the quantities. Never mind what Mr Scott thought, I'd impressed myself.

'There was quite a lot of it trickling out of my nose at 9.30 am, while I was out walking the dog, but I had no means of collecting it. Throughout the day (starting at 10.15, 12.15, 2.20 and 4.35) and evening (starting at 6.50, 9 and 10.45) I removed the liquid, which took two hours to do in total. The full amount was 31.75 ml, and it's sitting in a jug in my fridge! In no way was this all the fluid in my head at those times, but it was what I was able to collect, within the time that I had.'

I politely enquired whether this news would affect his view on the likely benefit of another ventilation tube operation, but I stopped short of asking how easy he would find it himself, to devote a couple of hours in his schedule to daily draining. It did tend to get in the way of work, socialising, care of children, and also, quite often, sleep. Moreover, a couple of hours constituted a good day. It usually took a lot longer than that.

I had started to mention to doctors that the severity of my symptoms, all of them, fluctuated from day to day, and were considerably worse on bad weather days – low barometric pressure, changeable, rainy, windy days, they were all very un-welcome, and during those spells I would have gladly dug a deep hole, and buried myself in it. This had been the case for very many months. I'd initially thought I must be imagining the link, and found the perplexed looks of doctors or friends in-creasingly embarrassing, if ever I rambled on about my weather preferences. During one of my regular internet searches, how-ever, I stumbled across a detailed study that confirmed what I thought.

Intracranial pressure, usually abbreviated to ICP, is the pressure inside the skull. In the 5th-4th century BC, Hippocrates of Kos had written about the effects of environmental factors on the psychophysical condition of humans, and the Polish scientists conducting the study were, for the first time, closely examining these effects on the body. They already knew that pronounced changes of atmospheric pressure were an unfavour-able stimulus for the human body, and they suspected that the more unbalanced the internal homeostasis of the person was, the more unfavourable those pressure changes became. The important conclusion, which entirely corroborated my own ex-perience, was that high values of atmospheric pressure (ranging from 770 mm Hg to 774 mm Hg on a mercury barometer) were shown to be by far the best for general equilibrium, with regard to pressure inside the skull (ICP), blood pressure, and blood supply to the brain. Below a certain border range of atmos-pheric pressure, all of these aspects of the body were adversely affected. It was clearly not a figment of my imagination – I had good reason to think of myself as barometer head.

A reply to my email whizzed back.

'I feel that we should try to analyse some of this fluid. I am at a meeting, and on honeymoon in the States, and I'm not back for a couple of weeks. I'll try to facilitate the investigation from abroad.'

Ah, so it was his *own* wedding – the one at which he'd said he'd got a little emotional. I might just have been prepared to put his cavalier attitude during my consultation down to newly married, thoughtless exuberance, had he not proceeded to bungle arrangements for the handling of the test sample. The extent of the bungling wasn't fully revealed until months later, the point at which I issued a formal complaint. Because of the earlier attempts to detect CSF fluid, I now knew I should keep the sample refrigerated, but I was unimpressed to find that no guidelines were given to me by Mr Scott, or anyone else. A container was delivered to my house in which to put the sample, my husband returned it to the clinic on his way to work, and several days later the results were interpreted by the consultant as indicating saliva rather than CSF. When I asked to see the test results in writing, I realised the laboratory had in fact found the result inconclusive, and had requested a further sample. I suggested I provide one, but my offer was rebutted by the consultant.

'The strong likelihood is that the fluid is saliva, and this should be the working diagnosis I feel,' wrote Mr Scott, now back from America. 'I will discuss your case with some colleagues to obtain further opinion, and ideas on how to proceed.'

Ten days later another email arrived, but only after prompting from me. 'I have written to Mr Pickering, and Mr Lello, with regard to this being a problem of over production of saliva. I will await their responses before offering further opinion. I'll need to see who has a special interest in such an unusual (in my experience) phenomenon. I honestly feel that we should not be hasty'.

There didn't seem to be any danger of that.

The facts of the matter were that Professor Lello and Mr Pickering (doctors nos.8 & 9) had already given their views, and by just sending a letter to the former, and copying it to the latter, Mr Scott was very unlikely to achieve anything. Nothing was done by him to elicit a response from these two consultants, and after receiving a couple of chasing emails from me, Mr Scott threw in the towel.

When the letter arrived at home, I scooped it up with excitement, hoping to read suggestions for the next step forward. I took it out, and read the words, 'I am not sure that I can really be of too much assistance.' The sentence hardly warranted the description of a letter. It had taken over two months for the doctor to tell me he didn't know how to help, and in the intervening period he had simply written to a couple of doctors I'd already consulted. I read the sentence over and over again, wondering if I'd missed something. All those wasted weeks, and absolutely nothing to show for it. The anger rose again, but my spirit sank. And then sank further, as the day progressed.

My faith in doctors had now reached such a low point that I was quietly beginning to have concerns about my mental state. I was heading down a path of ever-increasing disappointments, and I didn't have any idea which way to turn. No matter what I tried, or how hard I fought to get well, I was thrown back to where I started. Professor Rory O'Connor, who has researched suicidal behaviour for over twenty years, has charted the chain reaction that commonly occurs before a person sees no other way out of their wretchedness. It starts with the causes of trouble – pain, fear, hopelessness, hurt, failure, despondency, being let down; moves to the next stage – feeling trapped, despairing, overwhelmed, alone, disappointed; and then spirals downwards to the resulting outlook – defeat, lack of escape, no sign of rescue, loss of optimism, and very limited positive thoughts about the future.

I have a very sensitive core, despite the capable and determined exterior on display. I knew that I was a strong person, and I'd proved it to myself, but the downside to being strong was that people came to expect me to go on showing the same resilience, no matter what, or how many, hurdles were thrown in my way. Of course it was an unrealistic expectation – everyone has their breaking point. I was, in fact, now on Professor

O'Connor's downwards spiral, but no-one seemed to be aware of it. Although I knew perfectly well that, to millions of people, my life would seem enviable, despite its difficulties, that knowledge unfortunately didn't make coping any easier. It merely added a layer of guilt. The very fact that my mind had strayed, more than once now, to entertain the option of ending it, frightened me. I had never imagined I could harbour such thoughts.

It was the end of November, the time of the year when families make plans for Christmas, presents have to be chosen and purchased, and the calendar starts to fill up with festive events. Not so for me – my thoughts were focused on the workings of glands, and the hunt for Salivary Gland Mastermind of Great Britain. I found him by following a circuitous route through a GP, Professor Lello, and then another doctor that I wrote to in Cambridge. A few days before Christmas, there was a glimmer of hope once again. Hope tempered with doubt, however, as the new salivary specialist in his response cautioned: 'You appear to have a complex problem, and I am not sure of either the diagnosis, or how to treat your symptoms. I could offer a careful evaluation of the duct system, with two tests that can be done in a single day.' Not long afterwards, I was given a date for the NHS appointment, down in London again – it was nearly three months away, in March.

Another long, slow winter elapsed during which I made sure to keep busy, while I willed the weeks away. Apart from the local handbook I continued to publish, less frequently now, there were several new rooms to paint and decorate, as an extension at the back of our house was complete, with a bathroom adapted for our son's changing needs as he grew older. The painting proved an enormous challenge. Stretching up from a ladder, to reach ceilings and high corners, provided plenty of evidence of just how unbalanced I still was, and a fall from the ladder was only narrowly avoided on many occasions. I realised, too, that holding my arms up in the air, whether for painting, changing light bulbs, or hanging out washing, was something I could only tolerate for very short bursts of time.

This feeling had been creeping up on me, getting worse very gradually, and now it would take only a matter of seconds before I began to feel dizzy and sick, or even come close to passing out. It had become a very intense sensation.

Scouring the web for clues about my condition had become a regular activity whenever time permitted, and I remained convinced that a perilymph fistula (PLF) was part of the problem. I refused to believe what the British doctors had told me about my type of hearing loss not being associated with one. I came across an eyes-closed turning test, which a doctor had started using at the end of the 1970s, finding it very reliable in a group of his patients with potential fistulae. Interestingly, twenty out of the thirty-four didn't have hearing loss, so that study alone disproved what I'd been told. I enlisted my daughter's help, to enable me to try out the test without seriously injuring myself. Amy had to watch, while I walked along a corridor in our house with my eyes closed and then, as I turned around as if to walk back again, I had to stop and stand still. Amy was to be the judge of whether or not I swayed towards my left, the problem side. The result was a very conclusive yes, I did. In fact I had some trouble staying upright, and had to put out my arm to stop myself crashing into the wall. I added this to the information I was storing up, all proof that things were very far from alright when it came to the state of my head. Many times I felt like a lawyer amassing evidence for an upcoming trial.

As the March appointment was in London, I used the opportunity to spend the preceding day in Virginia Water, where I'd grown up. It is a small, leafy town on the outskirts of the capital. The long train journey up to Scotland was getting harder for my mother to undertake, so I didn't see her nearly as often as I would have wished. She was always concerned about my health, and how I was managing to cope with the care of her grandson at the same time. Seeing her gave me the chance to try to explain some of the complexities of my condition, but I underplayed the effects on me. She needed reassuring that my peculiar head wasn't her fault – I may not have been entirely convincing in my efforts, as no-one had yet established the root causes of SCDS. I couldn't offer an explanation as to why I had it, and my two sisters didn't.

On March 4, 2009 (almost six years on from the Amsterdam trip that had set in motion the whole series of events) I was introduced to Professor Russell (doctor no.11). He was a man of stocky build, with a round face and very firm handshake. I was warmly welcomed. The early impression I gleaned was of a busy and experienced physician, with a coterie of dental nurses, radiographers, assistants and junior doctors hanging on his every word, anxious to carry out his instructions, and play a useful role within his highly specialised team. R for revered.

I was assigned to Beth for the initial collection of saliva. Sucking a lemon drop encouraged its production, and then the flow could be measured, one side of my mouth compared to the other, and a sample sent away for analysis. The next stage of the visit involved a series of sessions utilising the most advanced scanning techniques. Two of the doctors carefully studied the screen over my head, as I lay still in the scanner at the end of the treatment, emitting little cries of excited astonishment at what they were seeing. The mood was catching; I could feel flutters of excitement myself. They were pulling out all the stops, so something surely had to be revealed with such a unique combination of sophisticated equipment, and highly skilled practitioners.

I sat alone in a corner of the waiting area, surreptitiously trying to remove some of the fluid build-up in my head, and keeping a watchful eye on the time, as my train home, at 5.30 pm from King's Cross station, couldn't be missed. At the end of the hospital lunch hour, I was summoned to hear the consultant's verdict. I walked into the small room, and to my dismay found a crowd of people. To the left was a gaggle of medical students, immediately invoking memories of the day Mr Bradford (doctor no.3) had announced my diagnosis, and to the right were assembled members of the team that had been dealing with my investigations. In the centre sat the professor, as though holding court, and behind him I could see my x-ray images propped up against a wall-mounted light box. I was asked to take a seat on the swivel chair in the middle of the room, directly opposite Professor Russell. I knew what the first question would be.

'Good afternoon. Are you ok with the students being here in the room? I can, of course, ask them to leave, if you aren't,' he said.

'Yes, it's ok,' I answered untruthfully.

'I was busy in theatre this morning, so I left it to my capable team to conduct the tests that we'd discussed. I've just been looking at the scans. We're all very pleased with the detail achieved in the x-rays, and you're one of the first patients to receive the benefit of our most recent piece of scanning equipment. There isn't another like it anywhere in the country.'

I didn't say anything, as I was keen to know what the exceptional scanner had shown. I already had the uncomfortable feeling I wasn't going to like what I heard. I suspected the doctors' excitement had been generated by the capabilities of their new toy, rather than the interesting finds it had been producing.

'So, we're absolutely certain that no link has been shown between your salivary gland and the ear, and there's no duct draining from the salivary gland into the ear, which would be highly unusual in any case. Your symptoms must relate to the inner ear condition you have, so there's nothing more we can do here. A sample of saliva is being sent away for analysis.' It was all very matter of fact. His team had done their job. My problem wasn't their problem. Nothing left to say.

Not for the first time, I was dumbfounded. I looked around the room, in the vain hope that someone would speak up, and tell me something that would help me. Everyone was staring at me, waiting for my response. Something inside me clicked, and there was a surge of annoyance.

I looked back at Professor Russell, and said sharply, 'I honestly don't know what to say. I am being sent round and round in circles by doctors, and I've had enough of it. I've been told the salivary glands are causing my symptoms, and now you're telling me they're not. Please tell me what I'm supposed to do.'

There were horrified faces to the left of me – no doubt the students had never heard a person talk to their consultant in such an accusing manner. I was way beyond caring what anyone in the room thought of me, and I was never likely to see them again anyway. My anger was increasing rather than lessening, and I carried on.

'I've explained to you and your team how I have to extract fluid from my head all the time, every single day. What is that fluid, if it's not saliva? CSF has already been ruled out – this has been going on for months and months. Do you think I'm imagining it?'

Professor Russell sprung up off his chair, and was now a few inches away from me. He was agitated and, thanks to my juvenile sense of humour, he reminded me of Rumpelstiltskin, the ridiculous little man jumping and hopping about in the fairy tale I loved as a child.

'From what you've told us, the test that was carried out by the last doctor doesn't sound conclusive. If the fluid was collected in your mouth, which I understand it was, it would have been contaminated by saliva. My suggestion is that you go back to ENT.'

'Contaminated by saliva?' I repeated, gormlessly. My brain was slowly processing what the doctor had just told me. 'Are you saying the test was meaningless, and wouldn't have been able to get an accurate result because of the way the fluid was collected from my mouth?'

'Yes, I am saying that. Anyone should have known that,' he retorted brusquely. 'I repeat – I suggest you go back to ENT.' The room was silent, relieved that the professor was back in charge.

I left the building in a daze, my head now throbbing with pain. A large double decker bus was rattling at a fast pace along the hospital approach road towards me, and I dearly wished a passer-by would push me into its path, and put an end to the nightmare.

It took about a week to haul myself up out of the depression. Several people contacted me to ask how the trip had gone, hoping I'm sure to hear some good news at last, but I short-temperedly replied that I was too fed up to explain in detail what had happened. No, it hadn't gone well, but the team had been very thorough, was my summary. It didn't take long before I realised that I wasn't actually cross with Professor Russell, even though as usual the scenario would have been so much easier to deal with if I'd been shown some understanding of my predicament. The real problem was that I was totally and utterly exhausted. It wasn't the kind of fatigue that could be rectified with a good night's rest. It was an all-encompassing physical and mental limpness. I was metaphorically sinking into sand, my body weighted down with heavy, wet clothes, sapped of all the energy I needed to drag myself out. My brain was fuzzy, my eyes wanted to close. I felt as though everything was shutting down.

After the week of avoiding communication, and inwardly searching for ways to regain my fighting spirit, I summoned enough energy to start rebooting my system. My first positive action was to order a testing kit to identify any possible food and allergy intolerances, and then I established contact with the laboratory that had analysed the fluid sample, enquiring whether there was any other means of solving the mystery source of the liquid. And, when I least expected it, something extraordinary happened. A shivers-down-the-spine, tingling-hairs-on-the-back-of-the-neck sort of something.

'I know exactly what is causing my problems, but it took me years to find out – it could be a possible cause for yours.'

It was as though the anonymous writer was personally addressing me. In one of my aimless meanderings around an online dizziness forum, the message had suddenly appeared on the screen. I read on.

'I had a cold, I went on an airplane, my nose and ears got all stuffy and pressurised, and that evening in the shower I blew my nose, and heard a pop in my left ear. I woke up the next morning, and was light headed and off balance.' It was a long posting, about a thousand words, and I rushed through it, eagerly devouring all the most pertinent comments: 'Doctors would always look in my ear and say, no, don't see any fluid'; 'fluid would come down the Eustachian tube'; 'fullness sensation in my ear'; 'I would repeatedly make scratching, sucking moves with my throat and mouth, to try and suck this fluid out'; 'it's constantly up there'; 'sensitive to loud noises'; 'eyes sensitive to light'; 'vague headaches'; 'my condition causes memory problems'; 'I have trouble concentrating, and anxiety'. And then further on, the crucial part: 'All doctors I went to were of no help, until I finally found the right one. The difference with him is like night and day, when it comes to inner ear problems. He did exploratory surgery and, sure enough, found inner ear fluid pouring out into the middle ear. And another thing, you do not have to have hearing loss to have a perilymph fistula like mine.'

And there, at the very end, was the doctor's name and location – Dr Owen Black, Portland, Oregon.

It was late on Saturday evening and, as so often with printers, it decided not to cooperate. I copied the message out by hand, word for word. I couldn't take the risk of such precious information disappearing as mysteriously as it had come to light. It was relatively easy to find Dr Black's contact details online, and I noted down an email address. The next day, during a call to a close friend who had been unwell, I told her about my discovery, and she urged me to write to the doctor. I explained why I was hesitant. I would have to devote my evening, once Patrick was in bed, to preparing a careful letter summarising everything that had occurred, and then there was a very high chance I wouldn't get a reply. Without revealing the depths to which I'd plummeted, I told her I knew I couldn't tolerate being let down by another doctor, not at the moment. And if he did reply, how could he help me anyway? He was in America after all, and I was in Scotland. She told me I would just never know unless I wrote – he might be my lifeline. She had no idea how appropriate her choice of word was. I knew what she said was true. I spent the whole evening preparing the four-page email. I pressed the send button before retiring to bed, and prepared for a very long wait.

12

MY LIFELINE

'As adults, it's seldom that a stranger can change the direction of our lives, but Dr Black is one who did that for me.'

Those are not my own words, but they could just as well have been. They were written in a moving online tribute to Dr Black, after he died unexpectedly in May 2012. F. Owen Black, M.D., a prolific writer on matters concerning the inner ear, and a very active clinician. His dedication to his work brought him into contact with NASA, and he helped start and fund the Vestibular Disorders Association.

And he stopped me from falling into the abyss.

There is an eight-hour time difference between Scotland and Portland, Oregon. My email was sent on Sunday evening, and at 1 pm the next day, perhaps during his lunch break, Dr Black sat down and typed out a reply to send to me. He had carefully read what I'd told him, and he answered every single one of my questions succinctly. Not only that, he picked up the telephone, and rang another doctor's office, with a view to discussing my situation. He told me that it was very likely that I had a perilymph fistula, bearing in mind what had happened on the flight in 2003, and the fact that I had in the meantime been diagnosed with SCDS made that even more likely – 'subjects with SCDS are more susceptible to PLFs.' He confirmed that 'they occur in normal hearing subjects', and he told me that he would 'make some enquiries about experienced surgeons in the UK.' He signed his letter 'with best wishes, Owen Black', and as a PS he added that he had just spoken with Dr Gerard Gianoli's partner in Louisiana.

The email, not least the swiftness of its despatch, bowled me over.

'I can't tell you how delighted I was to receive your message,' I told him. 'I have spent the last six years of my life battling with doctors here, trying to get them to answer my questions, and you managed to deal with everything in just a few hours. I am so very grateful to you.' And with the passing of time, the gratitude has intensified. If Owen Black hadn't gone out of his way to help me, a faraway stranger, I don't know what would have happened.

As Dr Black had advised me to do, the next day I sent the four-page summary to Dr Gianoli, just in case he was able to add to the information that had been provided by the Oregon otologist. It was more of an after thought. I wasn't particularly expecting anything important to come of it. I was, therefore, surprised and impressed to receive an immediate reply, elaborating on some of the answers I'd been given, and attaching a book chapter that Dr Gianoli had recently written on the subject of SCDS. He confirmed that he had also now spoken with Dr Black. The openness of these two American doctors, their willingness to share their knowledge, and their genuine desire to help me, was unlike anything I had witnessed on my medical path up to this point. The British doctors had kept their distance, corresponding with them by email was largely out of the question, and the pooling of knowledge among themselves was also something that seemed to be resisted. Every scrap of information I had had to drag out of them, as they took the strategy of providing it on a need-to-know basis to extremes. A very large part of the information I had acquired myself, without assistance from any of them. The early signs of a change of approach across the Atlantic were almost exhilarating.

The first message from Dr Gianoli also highlighted my ignorance. He made reference to the fact that his preference was for resurfacing the superior semicircular canal, thereby retaining its function, rather than the plugging which had been done to mine, effectively shutting down that balance canal. I had no idea this was an option – it certainly hadn't been offered to me, or even discussed. When I started thinking of the hole in the ruptured bone area as a hole in a tyre, it made perfect sense to me to close off the hole, like repairing a puncture. The bone, like the outer rubber tyre, is supposed to protect the soft inner tube beneath it. It was now clear to me that an SCDS patient had to be aware of more than one aspect when it came to surgery: the route through which the surgeon should enter their head (through the mastoid, or by means of a craniotomy, opening the skull to access the brain), and the type of repair (a plugging of the canal, or a resurfacing).

Our next email exchange was a revelation.

'A little known fact is that a large number of patients with vestibular disorders (not just SCDS, but others as well) will have concomitant panic and anxiety disorders. Panic attacks are the result of too much of a particular type of chemical surging through your blood stream (adrenalin and adrenalin-like chemicals). Anyone can get them, if the level of these is high enough. Interestingly, abnormal vestibular stimulation is a common trigger for their release.'

In those four sentences, Dr Gianoli had explained the last thirty years of my life. All the panic attacks, big and little, that had been eroding my confidence, holding me back at work, affecting my sociability, preventing me fulfilling my potential – in fact damaging every aspect of my life – had been happening for a specific reason. I hadn't been imagining them, and I wasn't going insane. It was the most satisfying and enlightening piece of news that I'd had for years. It seemed extraordinary that eleven British doctors had failed to mention it – was it a little known fact to them too?

When Dr Gianoli, several years later, gave the Grand Rounds lecture to the department of psychiatry, at the University of Chicago, he alerted them to the fact that their patients who were suffering from panic attacks may actually have inner ear disorders. Out of the thirteen indicators of a panic attack, only four are needed to make the diagnosis. Eight of the thirteen routinely happen during a vertigo spell: palpitations, pounding heart, or accelerated heart rate; sweating; trembling or shaking; nausea or abdominal distress; feeling dizzy, unsteady, light-headed or faint; feelings of unreality, or being detached from oneself; fear of losing control or going crazy; and chills or hot flushes. These indicators had been unwelcome visitors, popping in and out of my life, for a very long time.

Dr Carey Balaban, a neurobiologist in Pittsburgh, is researching the link between panic and dizziness, and sums it up thus: 'It's not a conscious decision. We believe there's some very basic wiring in the brain that underlies it.'

'If you would like to send me your records, I'd be happy to look through them and tell you what I think needs to be done,' wrote Dr Gianoli.

I took up his generous offer without hesitation, and within a couple of weeks I'd gathered all the material together, and sent it over to Louisiana. I still didn't have a plan in mind, I was just immensely thankful that someone was taking stock of things for me, and attempting to make sense of it all. Dr Black had stepped back, and seemed to have put the matter into the hands of his colleague, which was fine as far as I was concerned. When Dr Gianoli wrote to me again, after reviewing all the records, it was to convey some crucial information.

'I think you still have a problem with your left ear. Also, your scan has a finding suggestive of SCDS on the right side.' He explained in detail why my existing scans were inadequate for giving a more certain diagnosis, and also indicated that more definite recommendations could only be made by seeing me in person, and doing a thorough evaluation.

I was receiving a number of extraordinarily important pieces of advice in a relatively short period of time, and I hadn't yet digested it all. I certainly wasn't fully absorbing the fact that I might have another hole lurking on the right side of my head, and I focused on arrangements for the detailed CT scan that I planned to organise myself, using Dr Gianoli's specifications. I did, however, for the first time, plant the seed in my mind of actually going over to America for treatment, something I'd never even dreamed of doing up until then. I put my thoughts in an email.

'Once you have seen the new scans, I could then discuss with you whether it would still be appropriate for me to come over to see you. To be honest, I had not expected you to suggest that – partly because of the distance, but also because I'd imagined it would be inadvisable to travel on an airplane, shortly after an operation of this kind.'

Dr Gianoli's reply put paid to that worry. 'Air travel is a risk but, with appropriate precautions, it is a very low risk. We can discuss that later.'

The new scan was carried out without complication, the two radiographers tipping me up and turning me over in various directions, commenting that they had never received such exact instructions to follow. They seemed to relish the task, and nodded sagely when I commented that this was how it should have been done, at a different scanning facility, back in 2007. Of course they had no idea whether that was correct or not. To their knowledge, they'd never had a patient with a holey head before.

The CD was despatched to Louisiana, and in the interim I began to seriously consider the prospect of travelling all the way to the southern state for treatment. I kept my sisters informed of the rapidly changing developments, and in the middle of it all was my niece Alice's wedding. As with her brother's the previous year, it was a country wedding in a Suffolk village, and I travelled down with all members of my family to take part in the celebrations early in May. The wedding reception was a glorious occasion, in a large marquee decorated with bunting and flowers on the village green, just down the lane from my sister's thatched house. The sun shone on the idyllic scene. My imbalance prevented me from joining in the dancing, and the hustle and bustle of the large gathering was a big challenge to deal with. Conversations one-to-one were manageable, but inside the marquee with a lot of noise and numerous conversations underway, my head started to go into meltdown. It was a case of sensory overload, too much information coming in from all directions. However, my mood was positive and, although Patrick and I had to retire to bed fairly early, I enjoyed it.

My eldest sister, Georgie, mother of the bride, had by now read the letter I'd sent to Dr Black, explaining the sequence of events over the preceding six years. She told me how much it had upset her, and she was offering to go to America with me. She had reached the same conclusions – I couldn't risk any further surgery with a British doctor, after so many setbacks and oversights, and it would be out of the question for my mother to make the trip overseas. My husband would almost certainly need to stay behind because of his dialysis, and one of us really needed to be at home for Patrick. However, I stressed to my sister, who liked to have everything in life thoroughly organised well in advance, that I had to take things one step at a time, and not make any rash or hasty decisions. Apart from anything else, there was still a big subject to be tackled: How was I going to pay for it all?

The verdict arrived by email, when I was back in Scotland. 'From an anatomic standpoint you have dehiscence of BOTH superior semicircular canals.' I immediately recalled the unknown woman, for whom I had felt so sorry when my surgeon had told me about her two holes and the loss of hearing on her operated side. It wasn't until later that I discovered about fifty percent of SCDS patients are actually bilateral.

It continued: 'From the information that you have provided me, I am suspicious that you have bilateral symptomatic SCDS, and that the surgery was unsuccessful on the left side. I am also suspicious that you have a concomitant PLF on the left side. I cannot be more definitive without evaluating you. Scans vary in quality, and it is certainly possible that a prior scan may have looked less suspicious. For that matter, depending on how a scan is formatted, you can make a dehiscence (hole) appear, or disappear.'

Perhaps naively, I had considered all scans to be born equal. I certainly hadn't taken on board that the instructions given to the radiographer, and the quality of the output, could vary quite considerably, affecting the results achieved. The scanned images clearly needed to be reviewed, and manipulated, by someone adequately experienced to judge them.

I knew from what Dr Gianoli was telling me that accurate diagnosis depended on a medical history consistent with the disorder, a high resolution CT scan demonstrating the defect(s), and physiologic testing to corroborate this. But I also now knew in my heart of hearts that I *did* have bilateral symptomatic SCDS. For the very first time, I could make sense of everything. My left side had obviously become symptomatic as a result of the flight to Amsterdam, and quite possibly a perilymph fistula (so far undiagnosed) had been caused, in addition to the bone breaking through. My right side had, I believed, been symptomatic for years before that (also undiagnosed), and accounted for all the unsteadiness, dizziness, nausea, anxiety and, sometimes astonishing tiredness that I had always reasoned to myself must be part of my make-up, and needed to be silently tolerated. Now, at long last, there could be an explanation for it all.

Conveying this news to my mother wasn't going to be easy. I knew she would be devastated that I had more surgery in store, and that my head was considerably worse than I'd been led to believe. She already thought it was bad. Once I had explained the full situation, she was, however, very reassured to know that I had found such experienced and helpful doctors, and was equally relieved that my sister was planning to accompany me, and act as my nurse. The issue that wasn't up for discussion, she told me firmly, was that she was going to cover the cost of it all.

As if we didn't have enough to challenge us, people suffering from vestibular disorders usually encounter cognitive difficulties, malfunctions that are highly specific to most patients in this particular category. The psychiatrist Dr Kenneth Erickson, also in Portland, summarised these disturbances in a lecture he gave, based on a study of patients he had conducted in the 1990s, and his experience with hundreds of others since then. He gave a driving example, to show that multi-tasking presented a problem. There's a car approaching unexpectedly out of a left-hand turning, and another car coming along swiftly on the right-hand side. It is important to be able to monitor these two vehicles simultaneously, but with a vestibular problem that becomes very hard to do. I had frequently had such experiences, and avoided motorway driving as much as possible because of the number of moving vehicles. It had such a troubling effect on me that I sometimes developed an all-consuming desire to close my eyes.

He identified the difficulty his patients had in handling sequences, mixing up words and syllables in speech, reversing letters and numbers, even having trouble tracking the flow of a conversation at times. I had often wondered why, if someone gave me a telephone number to write down, I found it so troublesome to transfer those numbers, in the correct order, onto a piece of paper; I felt so stupid. When typing, I was frequently reversing letters in words, and then having to go back to correct them, and on many occasions I'd become Mrs Malaprop in a conversation, picking a close but unsuitable word, even though I knew it wasn't quite right, because I couldn't pinpoint in my mind the accurate one.

Dr Erickson stressed the decrease in mental stamina, concentration levels dipping quite dramatically, as well as in memory retrieval ability. Most of the time it might be possible to pull information out of the long-term memory store, but there was no longer a reliable rate for this. I was in no doubt at all that I had difficulty recalling, with accuracy, information gathered in the past, but events much closer to the present could equally well trip me up – I could blithely suggest to Hugh and Amy that we watch a certain television programme, or even be in the process of watching it quite happily, only to be told that I'd seen the very same programme a week earlier. And the final problem Dr Erickson highlighted was a decreased ability to grasp the bigger picture, and see the forest for the trees. He explained that even though many of those he tested were clever people, who did extremely well on their standard kind of psychological tests, they had lost the feeling of rightness, the satisfying internal feeling of 'yes, got that.'

All of these cognitive difficulties have a significant impact on simple, daily life functions, and so in many cases anxiety and depression follow. Dr Erickson attributed some of his conclusions to arguments put forward by the neurologist Dr Robert Grimm. He summed it up in an interview: 'It appears that what our brain needs, to function well, is unchanging accurate, balance-and-gravity information. And while the semicircular canals of the inner ear are the starting point, the signals from there go to the brain stem, and up into the brain in many different areas.'

In 2015 Dr Wackym, who took over Dr Black's practice when he retired, published a study which added supporting evidence. Seventeen patients were put through a series of neuropsychology tests, before and after surgical repair for SCDS. The tests (those after surgery being undertaken at three-month intervals) were designed to analyse their cognitive and neurobehavioural function, and overall there was a marked improvement. There was some variability, which may have been a result of the duration of the underlying disease before intervention, and a delay in the performance improvement in several patients seemed to suggest brain reorganisation.

This is a field in which much research remains to be undertaken, but all of Dr Erickson's views resonated with my personal experience. They also brought to mind several exercises that my husband and I had performed with Patrick after his thorough assessment at Brainwave, the charity working to unlock the potential of children with disabilities. The exercises to improve the function of his vestibular system, and hence his brain function, included standing him on a balance board, with curved rockers underneath that would pivot on their axes; gently spinning him back and forth in a swivel chair; and bouncing him up and down on a small trampoline.

Before making any commitment to an American expedition, I felt bound to make contact one more time with Mr Ingram, my Manchester surgeon. I had an opportunity to do so, as Dr Gianoli raised a query connected to my original scans, and also needed to know a little more about exactly how the doctor had carried out my surgical repair. The mention of a 'leading expert in the U.S.', in an email to his secretary, prompted an astonishingly rapid response from the doctor.

Having not once but twice discharged me, Mr Ingram was suddenly offering to see me again, if my symptoms in the left ear had recurred, whilst still maintaining that the original scans had been ok, and he therefore couldn't comment on my other ear. As far as I was concerned, there was very little he could do to make amends this late in the day, but the fact that he still believed the first set of scans were good enough, despite being informed that the new ones showed he had inaccurately diagnosed me, was enough to make up my mind. It could have been an easy choice for the surgeon to ask to see the new images or to liaise directly with the American expert to discuss the findings, but he chose to do neither. And I hadn't even bothered to tell him about the Americans' views on the perilymph fistula – I had better things to do with my time.

I was going to Louisiana.

13

ATLANTIC CROSSING

I had only been to America once before. For nearly ten years I had been in a relationship with a journalist, the younger brother of Anna Wintour, editor-in-chief of American Vogue. During a bitterly cold December in the 1980s, we had travelled to New York with a small group of friends to attend a wedding, and stayed in Anna's beautiful 19th-century townhouse in Greenwich Village. At that time the city was in the grip of a homeless crisis, and there was a disturbing contrast between the chauffeur-driven, opulent lifestyle of one world, and the bleak poverty of the other. During this ill-fated visit, I lost a large sum of money to a taxi driver, by wrongly identifying my American banknotes, which to an outsider all look very similar, and then contracted food poisoning from a salad lunch at a Bleecker Street café. I'd been barely well enough to attend the wedding reception. My hopes were pinned on a more successful American trip the second time round.

Baton Rouge, in southeast Louisiana, was going to be very different to New York. It has a semi-tropical climate and, as our visit was in July, we were expecting high temperatures and humidity. The capital of Louisiana lies on the Mississippi River, and is a major industrial centre of the American South. Its name, red stick, dates back to 1699 when French explorers caught sight of a red cypress tree, stripped of its bark, which marked a tribal boundary. I had not had any reason to learn about the place except that, by strange coincidence, I had just acquired a pair of chairs that had had to be shipped all the way over from there. My penchant for vintage Scandinavian furniture meant that I'd been delighted to win these items at a remarkably good price on eBay. They were by Hans Wegner, the undisputed master of Danish chair design. It was then that I had looked up the city's exotic-sounding name.

My sister, who is five and a half years older than me, was christened Georgina, but she has always been Georgie to me. Because of the age gap, we had moved into adulthood without ever spending large amounts of time together, apart from family summer holidays when we were both young. On leaving school, Georgie spent a number of years studying and working abroad. She was miraculously transformed, in my eyes, from a skinny, volatile teenager, prone to flare-ups with my parents and middle sister, into a confident, stylish, French-speaking mademoiselle. I watched the change with envy, keen to advance into her adult world. I'd been delighted to act as her bridesmaid when she married in her twenties, and I made a conscious effort to maintain close contact with her two children as they grew up. We had seen each other at regular intervals over the years, but we were now going to be spending a whole two weeks together. A steady trickle of emails and phone calls occurred, while we finalised all the arrangements.

I knew Georgie well enough to know that she was quite easily flustered and, perhaps taking after my mother, had a tendency to worry, so I decided to put together a large pocket organiser, with details for every eventuality: flight information, travel visas, car hire, directions for each journey we would need to take in and around Baton Rouge, hotel facilities, a book of street plans, local sights that she could visit while I was bedresting, even simple menus that could be compiled using our hotel microwave. I was so grateful to my sister for undertaking this trip that I wanted to make it as smooth and easy for her as

I possibly could. There was one aspect that was largely out of my control – her deep-seated fear of people vomiting.

'Good luck. I know you will be putting forth a lot of effort to come visit me, and I will do my best to make the effort worthwhile.'

Dr Gianoli's encouraging message set us on our way. I carefully followed the doctor's instructions to take oral decongestants for a couple of days before flying, and a nasal spray immediately before take-off, and descent. Georgie had a supply of chewing gum at the ready, for when the descent began. I now better understood what had gone wrong during the unfortunate Amsterdam weekend. The air in an aircraft is pressurised, but it's at a lower pressure than on land, which is why a passenger usually gets the feeling of a slight blockage after take-off. Pressure in the middle ear is equalised, whether at sea level or on a plane though, so long as the Eustachian tube is functioning, and has adequate time to do the equalising. It's almost never a problem going upwards, because the flow of air is from the middle ear out through the tube – a little like a balloon deflating. Coming down or landing in a plane, however, is harder, as the deflated balloon has to re-inflate. If the pressure change is rapid, that task of re-inflating becomes even harder. A problem can occur if the middle ear doesn't re-inflate, as the pressure differential at the ear drum will be great, and the pain caused intense. There are three minute bones called ossicles in the middle ear, and one of them, the stapes, could be driven into the inner ear, thereby causing a perilymph fistula. The slight cold I was suffering from, on my way to Amsterdam, had aggravated the situation and then, of course, my holey head had made things a damn sight worse.

After an exhausting day of travelling, with a change of flights at Atlanta, we checked into our suite at the hotel very late in the evening. Our accents didn't go unnoticed.

'Where y'all from?' asked the receptionist, with a welcoming smile.

My sister gave a quick summary, but then we retired, too worn out to enter into a long conversation. Compared to the miserable room in which I'd spent the night alone before my Manchester operation, we were now in the lap of luxury. There was a large bathroom with shiny, marble fittings, a bedroom with a big, soft, fluffy bed, a spacious living room with a pull out sofa bed (both rooms with their own televisions), and a fully equipped kitchen and eating area incorporated in the corner. We effectively had our own self-contained apartment. We were booked in for five nights, two of which my sister would be on her own while I was undergoing my operation, and then a further five nights in an identical suite that was out of town, close to the North Oaks Hospital, in Hammond.

After we had collected our hired car from the airport in the morning, we worked our way across the sprawling city to the Ear and Balance Institute. It was creeping up to 90°F outside the car, but the air conditioning was blasting out on the inside. I did not envy my sister, having to get used to driving the unfamiliar, automatic Hyundai, on what was to us the wrong side of the road, and weave it in and out of busy lanes of fast-moving traffic on the Interstate Highways. Huge trucks with smoke stacks were roaring past her. I was trying to help direct her from A to B with the step-by-step instructions I'd printed out back home. We made a few unplanned detours, but pulled up on time in front of the tall office building in which Dr Gianoli had his private practice, together with his partner Dr Soileau.

I signed our names in the book at the reception desk, and introduced myself to Val, the very likeable assistant, with whom I'd shared several emails and phone calls. She showed me into a room to wait for the surgeon. It was an almost bare room with no clues to the owner's personality, just a solitary watercolour hanging in a corner, a peaceful scene of a rowing boat at its mooring. I was just about to launch myself across the room to look at it closely, when the door swung open. A smiling doctor, dressed in a brown suit and crisp, white shirt, introduced himself.

'Good morning. How are you? How was your flight?'

He became even more personable as he spoke, the pleasant lilt of his accent giving his words an agreeable quality. I was momentarily taken back, as I had mistakenly switched the doctors' photographs in my mind, and had been expecting to meet a greying, bearded man, who must have been Dr Soileau.

'I'm fine, thank you. We arrived very late last night, so I'm just a little tired. I left my home in Scotland two days ago.' I handed over the questionnaire I'd been given to fill in.

Dr Gianoli listened very attentively, while he talked me through all the details I'd written on the form.

'We're going to start things off with some tests with Kacie, our audiologist,' explained Dr Gianoli, 'and then after lunch they'll be some more tests, which I'll be handling myself. I'll see you later on.'

'Is it correct that the office closes for an hour at lunch time?' I asked.

I was checking this specifically for Georgie, as it was weighing on my mind that it was going to be a tedious wait for her, with so many hours to pass on her own, while I was undergoing a very comprehensive series of tests which would take over a day to complete. The VEMP and hearing tests would need to be repeated, but all the others were entirely new to me.

'Yes Ma'am. I do like to eat,' he said with a broad smile.

It was going to take me a while to acclimatise myself to the frequent use of this term among Southerners, as it produced a slightly uncomfortable feeling being addressed in what sounded to me a deferential manner.

The morning's audiology tests were straightforward; almost relaxing, when it came to one which involved me lying back in a recliner, while gentle, clicking noises were transmitted into my ears. But things started to hot up after lunch. A rotating chair, a platform test which involved me wearing a harness like a parachute jumper to prevent me falling over, and a blacked-out chamber with tiny, coloured lights to track with my weary eyes, were just some of the hurdles. I had to be released from the chamber for a while, as I was on the brink of liberating the bowl of soup I'd had for lunch. As the day wore on, the nausea became constant (this and the chamber incident I kept secret from my sister, with whom I sat intermittently in the waiting area, while I rested briefly between tests), and aches and pains gradually permeated my whole body – a lethal combination of jetlag, physical exertion, and debilitating levels of concentration and brain strain.

For the tests involving Dr Gianoli, the familiar bug-eyed monster goggles reappeared, and cold or warm water was alternately streamed into my ears, to determine whether either would induce spinning. As far as I was aware, it hadn't yet been established whether or not I definitely had SCDS on my undiagnosed (right) side, but that was about to change. The busy doctor had left the room to attend to another matter, but I could hear his footsteps approaching along the corridor, as I lay on the bed (still begoggled), awaiting his return. Val was already in the room.

'Ok, sorry about that,' he said as he came in. 'Now, please just stay lying flat, and try to relax as much as you can. Val and I will make sure you stay safe.'

At the back of my neck on the right-hand side, a fast and furious vibrating movement burrowed into my skin, and a second later all hell let loose. It was the speediest and most severe attack of vertigo I had ever experienced, and my loss of control was total. I fixed my sight on the grey ceiling as it whirled above me, I gripped the sides of the bed, and I let big teardrops freely roll down my cheeks under the goggles. I felt the surgeon lower his warm hand firmly on top of mine, and the accumulated loneliness and desperation of the last few years swept over me, the simple gesture becoming transformed into a gentle kindness of almost excruciating depth. It revealed the extent of the pent-up emotion that was looking for release. I later read an article by a medical student at the end of his first year, in which he had attended a course exploring the interpersonal fabric that exists between physician and patient. When would touching be deemed an intrusion into the patient's personal space, the course questioned? The student had found himself in a situation with a tearful person, struggling to cope with the recurrence of a serious illness, and had taken his hand to confer a wordless message of support and encouragement. The male patient had been consoled and comforted, and so had I.

'Did you see that?' Dr Gianoli said to Val, his hand still resting on mine, while the spinning was slowly winding down. 'We got a very similar result on the patient we saw last week, when we used this bone conduction vibrator.' The pair of them had been watching the brisk, rotational eye movements, enlarged by the goggles, which had been triggered by his testing device. There was no question that I had a hole on my right side, as already indicated on my scan.

'Good. That's all fine,' the doctor said. 'Will you be alright now? Val will take over, and I'll see you again in the morning. I hope you get some rest back at your hotel.'

And I did. I insisted on taking the sofa bed because my sister was a poor sleeper, and needed the best chance of a good night in the proper bedroom adjoining the bathroom, but she would only agree on the understanding we switched over in the next suite, which would be after my operation. After fitting in an early morning MRI scan, as my surgeon needed to be sure he had one that covered my whole brain, I completed the remaining tests back at the Ear and Balance Institute.

I was interested to learn that the doctors had an unusual piece of equipment on the premises, one that had been invented by Dr Robert Marchbanks, a Consultant Clinical Scientist at Southampton University. The British scientist had devised a groundbreaking test (tympanic membrane displacement/TMD) to measure the pressure level of someone's cerebrospinal fluid, which could potentially replace the need for an invasive lumbar puncture. NASA had already purchased the device, concerned about the health of their astronauts, as over half had shown some visual changes during flight, and three were permanently impaired. In 2012, NASA and the Ear and Balance Institute were able to collaborate on a research study, to help prove the utility and safety of the equipment. After careful analysis of more than a thousand of the institute's patients' results from TMD, alongside about six hundred lumbar puncture results taken on the operating table, Dr Marchbank's invention was approved for use on the International Space Station, putting him at the forefront of space medicine. (Interestingly, in SCDS patients the numbers did not correlate.) In July 2009, I was more than happy to be wired up, so that my CSF reading could be checked in Dr Gianoli's office. It showed a slightly abnormal result. The procedure was completely painless, which my lumbar puncture in Manchester had most certainly not been.

With all the test results in and discussed, a decision was made. I definitely needed revision surgery on my left side, and this time my head would be opened up in two places – not just through the mastoid, opening up the scar left by Mr Ingram, but also via the skull. I was having the craniotomy I'd thought I'd successfully avoided. There was a very good reason though, as my previous surgeon had omitted to point out that the first method had given him limited manoeuvring room, and the visualization of the area being worked on was greatly reduced. Dr Gianoli needed a full view of what was going on inside my head, so that he could repair a likely perilymph fistula, look for a possible CSF leak, and make sure the hole in the semicircular canal was properly dealt with this time, to prevent a further recurrence of symptoms.

Before I signed all the necessary paperwork for my surgery very early the next morning, Dr Gianoli broke some worrying news.

'You wrote on the form that you'd been taking Ibuprofen to help with your headaches. I presume you've stopped that now?'

I was curious to know why the question was relevant at this point. 'Yes. I think I took one on my first day of travelling, but haven't had any since,' I said. 'So it's been three days now.'

Dr Gianoli furrowed his brow. Something was obviously on his mind. 'Ibuprofen is one of the medications that can create a problem for blood to clot. That is a matter of some concern, as you're about to have a craniotomy. It's probably something we should have mentioned before you came over. Are you going to North Oaks for your pre-op this afternoon?'

'Yes, we're going there after we leave here. I've spoken to them about it, and they're expecting me,' I replied.

'Good. I think they're going to have to do a test to check your bleeding time. We'll have to hope it's ok, but I'm afraid if it's not, we can't take the risk of surgery.'

Dr Gianoli maintained his relaxed composure as we parted company. He didn't seem overly concerned about the situation, unlike me. In the car I relayed the conversation to my sister.

'I just can't believe that we've come all the way over here to Louisiana, I'm about to have brain surgery, and now there's a possibility it can't proceed because of a headache tablet I took a few days ago. Georgie, what are we going to do if they say it can't go ahead?'

My sister didn't need to say very much in reply, her anxious expression said enough. We set out on our new expedition, heading directly east out of the city along Interstate 12, in the direction of New Orleans. Georgie wisely suggested we time the drive of over fifty miles to the hospital, as we had to be there no later than 5.30 am the next morning, and we'd been told there was a speed restriction, closely monitored by police, along that stretch of road. North Oaks Medical Centre, one of the largest hospitals in Louisiana, was set outside the town of Hammond, and we needed to be sure we had worked out how to find it easily.

Inside the main building within the modern complex, the enormity and strangeness of my situation began to sink in. It was a huge, light-filled construction that had grown from a sixty-bed facility in the 1960s, to one with 237 beds; the imposing pillars around the entrance, the expanse of dazzling white, curved surfaces, the giant panes of glass, and the sheer spaciousness were impressive, but also somewhat intimidating. I was more at home with a scruffy, concrete entryway, with the smokers in their dressing gowns. Once I had got past the process of being fully registered as a patient, and had established that my long-distance payments had gone through, I waited to be seen by the nursing staff for all my pre-op checks. The blood work had been done back in Scotland, but among other things an EKG was needed to check the electrical activity of my heart, as well as the test to see whether the Ibuprofen was going to bring everything to a halt.

'Philippa. That's a real pretty name', the nurse said, as I was shown into a small side room. 'And you've come all the way from Scotland, is that correct? Has someone accompanied you?'

'Yes, my sister's waiting outside. I've come all this way because I have a very rare condition, and you have one of the best specialists in the world for dealing with it, here in Louisiana.'

Her eyes brightened, and she looked down at the paperwork. 'Ah yes, I see your physician is Dr Gianoli. We always hear very favourable comments about him. Now, your blood pressure and the EKG results are fine, but I think you know we've been asked to do a check on your bleeding time. Just hold out your finger please, I'm going to give it a little prick. You shouldn't feel very much.'

She looked up at the clock on the wall above us, and then down at the tiny speck of blood rising up out of my hand. She continued talking, as though it was perfectly usual to puncture someone's skin while conversing with them.

'And is your sister going to be looking after you, once you leave the hospital, Philippa?'

She was watching the second hand of the clock as it worked its way around the circle, then glanced at me, as the little red mound grew ever larger. The nurse hadn't told me for how long we had to monitor its progress, but I could feel my heart beating hard, in fear of what she would tell me once the time was up.

'Yes, I have to stay in the hospital for two nights, and then when I come out she will be looking after me while I rest in bed for another three days. Can I ask you, does taking Ibuprofen make a big difference to how the blood clots?'

'I think studies have shown that the blood loss is approximately double for those using the medication,' she answered. 'That's why doctors usually advise that it should be stopped about seven to ten days before certain types of surgery.'

My heart began to thump faster. How much longer until I knew the worst?

She let go of my hand, and grabbed a ball of cotton wool from the shelf.

'There we are. That's ok, you're within the acceptable time limit,' she said.

She smiled at me while removing her latex gloves, watching the relief from her announcement spread over my face. Once the paperwork was complete, and contact details provided for an emergency, the nurse wished me all the best for my operation. I hastened out to the entrance lobby to give Georgie the good news.

We could now head straight back to our hotel, and relax. As we got closer to Baton Rouge, the storm clouds that had been gathering along the highway grew darker, and more menacing-looking. Within minutes, they erupted with a heavy downpour, which then increased in tempo until the windscreen wipers were struggling to fend off the drenching. Georgie switched on the headlights, and we carefully and slowly navigated our way into the city, trying to follow the route to the hotel that had been gradually becoming familiar to us. The water fell from the sky in torrents, and then stopped very suddenly, just as we were pulling into the car park. Within seconds the sun was shining again. It was a weather pattern that would repeat itself quite frequently during our stay.

I slept surprisingly well, and was woken by the sound of my sister rustling around in the room next door, and then coming past my sofa bed to make herself a cup of tea. I wasn't able to have anything in the way of food or drink, but I'd allowed time for a good scrub clean in the bath. We'd decided to set aside an hour for the journey, and that meant setting off at 4.30 am. It was only half-light when we slipped past the unmanned reception desk, and outside to the car.

My sister stopped and stared. There were two identical cars parked next to each other, where the evening before there had only been ours. They were a distinctive colour, a shade of paint I've since seen described by a disgruntled customer as morning piss gold. She pointed the key at the one she thought belonged to us, but nothing happened. She tried the other gold car, and still nothing happened. I could sense the panic starting to build up, as my sister now fumbled around in her handbag, hunting for her glasses. The glasses fell out of the bag onto the tarmac, and in the grey early morning light it was difficult to see where they'd fallen. Between the two of us we recovered them, and then Georgie managed to open the first car by putting the key into the lock. She tried the ignition, and the car failed to start.

'What's going on? This must be our car, we've got inside it,' she said. 'Why isn't it starting?'

Georgie's face was crumpled with concern and frustration, whereas I felt strangely serene, as though I simply couldn't afford to let myself feel any stress before the head surgery.

'Is there anything you aren't doing quite right?' I asked her. 'Is everything switched on that should be switched on? I know what you're like Georgie, once you start to panic you may be missing something obvious.'

I peered at my watch. 'Don't worry about the time, just calm down, and let's try once again from the beginning,' I suggested. I *was* worried about the time, but I didn't want her to know that.

Georgie went through the starting process several times again, but the car wasn't budging. It was time to accept we were stuck in Baton Rouge, and I would soon be expected in an operating theatre an hour's drive away. We were also locked outside the hotel, and had to bang hard on the glass door to attract the attention of a staff member who seemed to be the only person up at such an early hour. We needed the man to call any local taxi firms he could think of to come to our aid, and after a very tense twenty minutes of explaining, cajoling, advising and then waiting, a bright yellow cab pulled up outside the hotel. The morning was starting well for the driver, who was required to deliver me to the hospital, and then return all the way back again, to deposit my sister at the hotel where there was a car needing to be fixed.

It was a mad dash to Hammond, but not as mad as we would have liked because of the speed restriction, which the taxi driver made clear he had no intention of breaking. The risk of being pulled over by the police was too high. He dropped me at the hospital entrance, and I scrambled out of the car.

'Bye, Georgie. Please don't worry. I'm sure I'll be fine. Remember to call the hospital later on, unless Dr Gianoli calls you first', I said as I dragged my overnight bag off the back seat.

'Thank you so much for your help. Please can you take my sister back to the hotel now,' I added, looking at the driver. I was well aware that this was the antithesis of the type of hospital admission my sister had planned for me, but there wasn't a moment to lose. I rushed into the building, checked myself in at the ground floor desk, and dived into the first lift that opened up.

Two teenagers stepped in seconds after me. Their heavy make-up and youthful looks didn't suggest they were hospital staff, and yet no indications of imminent surgery were apparent either. It was far too early to be on the premises for any other reason.

'Did you just arrive in that yellow taxi cab?' the blonde-haired girl asked me, looking me up and down, as though eyeing something in a shop window.

'Yes. I had to, as our car had broken down. My sister was supposed to be driving me here.'

Their jaws dropped and their eyes widened. 'Oh. My. God. Where are you from?' the other one asked, and they looked at each other, sniggering in astonishment. As soon as I mentioned Scotland, the blonde exploded with glee.

'I've never seen a yellow cab before today, and I've never been outside Louisiana either. And you live in Scotland,' she drawled. 'I love how you speak.'

The lift stopped at my floor, and I backed out, putting up my hand as a farewell gesture. I could hear their giggles, as the lift door closed behind me. I was late but not too late, and I hurried through to be prepared for my theatre visit. The combination of the Ibuprofen scare and the dramatic car episode had left me eager for some peace and quiet on the operating table. It wasn't until after my deep slumber that I found out it was Louisianan weather that had jinxed us – the headlights turned on in the downpour, hadn't been turned off again. Left on all night, the battery was as flat as a pancake.

14

OPENING UP THE SKULL

Dr Gianoli is a neuro-otologist – an amalgam of an ear doctor, and a brain surgeon. Another brain surgeon, Henry Marsh, in an interview on British radio, described what Dr Gianoli would have seen when he opened up my skull: 'The surface of the living brain is very shiny, covered in beautiful filigree of blood vessels; and the spinal fluid also shines very brightly if you're using the microscope.' The neuro-otologist wouldn't be delving inside what Mr Marsh likened to 'slightly firm white jelly', but he would need to do some delicate manoeuvring of the section of the brain called the temporal lobe (behind the temples), to access certain areas of my head. The human hand is a marvel of dexterity, and nimble fingers are certainly required for surgery within the inner ear, a space about the size of an American dime, and for exploration of the superior semicircular canal, a bone no thicker than a toothpick.

'So, you're from Scotland. Wow, do you live near Edinburgh Castle? I'd love to go see it. I adore all that history stuff. How old is the castle?'

Was I dreaming, with a uniformed American at the forefront of the action, or was I still in the intensive care unit, only half awake, being cross questioned about Scottish history by an animated male nurse?

'Oh, I'm afraid I really don't know. There are so many different parts to it,' I replied, struggling to assemble words into a sentence, let alone provide accurate historical data.

I *was* still in ICU, my head heavily bandaged, and the young nurse was changing one of the bags for the intravenous drip. I'd made it through the night, drifting in and out of sleep while a blood pressure pump on my arm automatically inflated and deflated, and a machine attached to my calves massaged them to keep blood circulating through my legs. At some point during the stupor, Dr Gianoli may have paid a visit, but that could equally well have been a dream.

When I next woke up, breakfast was being served. It was solid food, albeit soft and mushy, and I wasn't sure how my sore jaw would cope. In Scotland I was partial to a bowl of porridge, but now I was having my first taste of grits, the southern states' equivalent – a ground corn mixture that is often served at breakfast. I spooned in small amounts, followed by a few scoops of faded yellow scrambled egg, and then washed it all down with some apple juice. The effort in doing so caused me to nod off again.

Still in the same bed, but with various wires and the catheter removed, I found myself in a hospital room later the same morning, with little recollection of how I had got there. It was a second surreal awakening, as to my surprise there was another patient in the room, hidden from me behind a thin, floral curtain. The drapery was bulging in various places, as there was a group of people, presumably family members, gathered around the bed, murmuring their prayers together, and then breaking into songs of praise. A wavy-haired man at the end of the bed, wearing a t-shirt emblazoned *Addicted to Jesus*, wished me good morning.

'You look great. How are you feeling? I looked in on you in ICU but you were sound asleep.'

I raised my heavy head, and saw the speaker was Dr Gianoli, the blue, cotton scrubs from our last meeting now replaced with a polo shirt and casual trousers. He looked cheerful and refreshed. He scratched his nails across the hard, protective shell, which was underneath my bandage.

'Can you hear that?' he asked. I nodded.

'Good. Everything went well yesterday,' he said. 'But you did give me a few surprises.'

'Oh dear, that doesn't sound too good. What sort of surprises?'

'Just some things I wasn't expecting to find,' he explained. 'An encephalocele, which is a herniation of brain tissue; a rather nasty, oily mess in the tip of your mastoid, which I had to completely clear out; a piece of broken-off bone floating around, presumably from your previous surgery; a small cholesteatoma in your ear canal – I'm surprised I hadn't noticed it when I examined your ear in the office chair; and you did have a CSF leak. It was gushing through actually.'

I lowered my head back down, and smiled up at him. I was aware that my response was muted; I felt drained of energy, and couldn't summon excitement because of the dampening effect of all the drugs in my system. I could only absorb a limited amount of information, but deep inside a satisfying sense of relief was permeating. The surgeon's words had just delivered my vindication. Flickering through my mind were the nineteen interminable months spent traipsing from doctor to doctor after my first operation, being told at all the vital stages that they could find no objective signs to corroborate what I was telling them. Resentment was stirring again. I wished I could magically transport those doctors across the ocean, arrange them like my little puppets around the bed, and have them listen to Dr Gianoli recounting his findings. Might they at last admit they got things wrong, that they should have done something to help me?

'A cholesteatoma, is that something to be worried about?' I asked.

'It's a little mass of skin growing backwards behind your eardrum,' he said. 'No, nothing to worry about at all, it was easy for me to remove.'

It wasn't until much later that I discovered a number of ways that such a growth can form in the middle ear, the most common of which is when negative pressure builds up in there – the kind that had been showing on my tympanometry test results in Manchester. Over time, the eardrum begins to retract back towards the inner ear, and eventually the cholesteatoma forms, and continues to grow. If left unattended, that is when it does become something to worry about, as it can cause infection, and eventually bony destruction.

When Georgie arrived later in the day, I was able to pass on the positive news that the prognosis was very good. Dr Gianoli expected me to make an excellent recovery. My sister's role as nurse was now an essential part of that process, and she seemed to relish the task. One of her first jobs after my second night in the hospital was to pay a visit to the large Walmart store she'd located nearby, to collect a pile of prescriptions, among them some medicated drops that would need to be administered regularly into my ear; coming from a country with a national health system, and even free prescriptions where I lived north of the border, the shockingly high, accumulated costs of the items was not something we'd prepared for.

Georgie helped me get ready for the drive back to our hotel, where I was going to be under strict instructions to remain in bed for the next few days. Her protective instinct came to the fore before we departed, as one of my roommate's visitors, standing at the end of my bed, tried to engage us in a lengthy conversation about SCDS symptoms. I began by answering her pressing questions, talking softly out of the corner of my mouth, but I soon found the volume and pitch of her voice very discomforting, and her gesticulations too quick and tiring to watch. I started to fade away and disengage from the encounter, which my sister was quick to spot. She took over the conversation, and then politely explained that I needed to rest before our journey.

It was Saturday when we left the hospital. I was helped into a wheelchair, and a friendly nurse pushed me along into the lift, depositing me down in the large vestibule, which was bustling with the weekend visitors coming and going. My sister had gone on ahead to bring the car, its battery now recharged, directly outside the entrance. Waiting by the doorway, I inhaled deeply, drawing in the steamy afternoon air, and the fragrance of the citrus shrubs planted nearby. It was refreshing to be in the open again, but the few minutes were enough in my fragile state. I felt less vulnerable once stretched out on the rear seat inside the car, cushioned within the nest of pillows that my sister had piled up for me. I shaded my eyes from the alternating strips of bright light and shadow, as we drove past shops and houses, Georgie repetitively asking from the front, 'Are you ok? Am I going too fast? Do you feel alright?'

Once ensconced in the hotel, my big sister took charge of all my needs. She lay all the medications out on the table – ear drops, anti-nausea tablets, antibiotics, painkillers, stool softeners; drew up a timetable for when each one needed to be taken; provided me with regular drinks; helped me in and out of bed to get to the bathroom; monitored my watching of television (short bursts of visual stimulation were all I could endure), or listening to the radio, to ensure I wasn't overstretching myself; and answered any phone calls. One of the calls was from Dr Gianoli asking whether, as strangers in the country, we would welcome a visit. We declined his offer, both of us remarking afterwards on the generosity the doctor showed with his time.

I had brought over in my suitcase a selection of dried savoury Miso soups, the comforting staple of Japanese cuisine, which my friend Jan had suggested could nourish me back to good health. Georgie prepared the liquid meals for me, usually with an accompanying selection of oatcakes or bread, and small pieces of soft fruit or vegetable. On the few occasions my sister left me alone, to get some shopping, take a quick dip in the outdoor pool in the hotel grounds, or simply have a break from being stuck within our two rooms, she kept a watchful eye on the time; she never wanted me to be left unattended for too long. She flatly refused to go out exploring, visiting any local places of interest. I couldn't have asked for a more conscientious or considerate carer.

It was a moment of excitement and apprehension when the time came for the bulky bandage to be removed. Georgie and I carefully unwrapped my head, and I then insisted she describe its appearance to me, as I hadn't the confidence yet to take a look in the mirror. I'm not sure what I was expecting to see – a bloody, gaping hole in the side of my skull? The incision, in fact, ran several inches down through a section of shaved hair above my ear (the craniotomy part of the surgery), with metal staples holding everything firmly together, and then carried on behind the back of my ear, where Dr Gianoli had reopened the cut that Mr Ingram had made. Georgie assured me it all looked clean and tidy, despite the matted clumps of hair, and everything was healing nicely.

Thursday morning was the scheduled post-op appointment back in Baton Rouge. As I needed to get more used to being up and about, we'd already gone out for a short drive the previous day, meandering further south towards Mandeville and Lake Pontchartrain, to take a wander by the waterfront, and look at some of the local properties with their inviting porches, and bright white, clapboard exteriors. While I was taking my time, slowly getting washed, I started to recognise the familiar signs – sweaty palms, a clammy forehead, the deathly pallor creeping over my face, followed by rolling waves of nausea – that precede a vomiting attack. I steadied myself against the washbasin. The door to the adjoining sitting room and kitchen was closed, and it crossed my mind that I could perhaps get through the episode without my sister being any the wiser. My breakfast made its swift exit. I flushed the toilet, and leaned up against the solid mahogany headboard on the bed, still wobbly and faint.

Georgie must have special built-in, anti-vomit antennae. She knocked and entered the room, enquiring how things were going, and whether I would soon be ready to leave for the city. She only had to take one look at me to guess what had just occurred. I knew it would take all my powers of persuasion to convince her that it was nothing more than an unfortunate passing incident, and I would now be perfectly fine. Being physically sick was a more disturbing event than that in my sister's mind, and one she had spent a considerable part of her life doing her best to avoid. How she had engineered that, bringing up two children apart from anything else, I still found it hard to comprehend.

Georgie explained to Val on the telephone that there had been a slight setback, and the appointment was duly rescheduled for the afternoon. It's not at all uncommon for a person to throw up after a surgery, and even a week later (the amount of time that had elapsed in my case) the body can still be reeling from the shock of major trauma such as a craniotomy. In less than an hour, however, I had completely recovered my composure, and having lost my first meal of the day I was looking forward to a light lunch before we went on our way. Georgie had other ideas. And it presented a problem, inasmuch as she was the one in charge of our food supplies. Over the next forty-eight hours, until she was sufficiently assured that it had been a one-off occurrence, a battle had to be waged, to persuade her to allow me to eat normally again.

The sickness hadn't unduly worried me, so long as nothing had been disturbed in the healing process, but another matter was preying on my mind. I still had an ear full of packing, everything on the left side of my head was numb, and the internal swelling would take weeks to subside, but I now had a nasty suspicion that there was fluid lurking in there that simply shouldn't exist, regardless of all the surgery mayhem. I told my sister of my concern before we left the hotel. At the Ear and Balance Institute, the packing material was taken out of my ear canal, stitches and staples removed with minimal discomfort, and Dr Gianoli determined, after examining my eyes, that some repositioning of the crystals in my balance canals would be in order. I was still getting regular bouts of vertigo, as I rolled from side to side in bed. I knew what to expect, having had these Epley manoeuvres (named after the American otologist who invented the procedure in 1979) carried out in Manchester, but I was given useful new advice this time: to sleep with my head upright for the next seventy-two hours, so as not to undo the work of the repositioning. This seemed to tie in rather neatly with an economy, long haul flight the next afternoon, on which it would be virtually impossible to sleep in any other, more comfortable, position.

I couldn't depart without raising the subject of the dreaded fluid. But I also anticipated the response before it was delivered.

'Remember, you only just had your surgery a week ago. You've got to give everything time to settle down. It's going to take a while. There's every reason to think you'll make an excellent recovery.'

The surgeon held my gaze for a few seconds. Then he added, 'Would you like to take something for the flight home, in case you start to feel nauseous again? There's a patch I can give you for that – you just need to apply it to the side of your neck before the journey. It lasts about three days.'

Georgie had joined us in the consulting room, keen to be involved in the discussion, as well as the exchange of goodbyes. She jumped straight in with the answer. 'Yes, she would please, Dr Gianoli. I think that would definitely be a good idea.'

Scopolamine. Better known as Devil's Breath in Colombia, where it's extracted from the local borrachero tree, and has been seen to induce a zombie-like state, as the key component in an extremely dangerous drug. Under the brand names Transderm Scop, Scopace or Maldemar, however, scopolamine is widely available as a skin patch about the size of a dollar coin, and is used to prevent nausea and vomiting caused either by motion sickness, or recovery from anaesthesia and surgery.

None of us, Dr Gianoli included, could have foreseen the pivotal role this unassuming little sticking plaster would play in coming months.

15

WALK, WALK, WALK

In normal circumstances, the outer ear collects sound waves, and then directs them into the ear canal, and down to the eardrum. The eardrum vibrates, and the resulting tremors reach the three tiny bones in the middle ear. These miniature bones amplify the sound vibrations, and transmit them to the cochlear of the inner ear, where they are converted into electrical impulses, to travel from the acoustic nerve to the sound-processing region of the brain.

Business as usual hadn't yet resumed on the left side of my head, however, and there were numerous sounds that were undergoing a transformation. The busy airports of Atlanta, our stopover, and London Heathrow, our destination, seemed to have been infested with dozens and dozens of Minnie and Mickey Mice, large and small, their cases often clattering along behind them, their abnormally tinny, squeaky voices pinging in and out of my ears, causing my head to vibrate, and my eyes to jump with the distortion. The PA system, bellowing out from time to time, intensified the experience. I'd handled the bangs, bumps, hums, whines, rushes of air, jet engine thrusts, and all manner of electrical and mechanical noises that emanate between departure gate and arrival lounge, and now there was a new set of visual and auditory stimuli to withstand. Fortunately,

I'd anticipated that the crowded concourses would present a significant challenge just eight days after delicate inner ear surgery, so at both stages of the journey I was sitting securely in a wheelchair, being steered through the mouse glut.

The patch had successfully warded off any further sickness, and its drowsy side effect had helped induce sleep during the long flight. I washed my hands thoroughly as I removed it, heeding the warning that if scopolamine were to make its way into my eyes there was a strong likelihood of blurred vision and dilated pupils – a mad, staring look, to accompany my slow-working brain, which was feeling the after-effects of being nudged around in surgery.

Once safely back home in Scotland, I gradually began to build up the series of regular exercises that constituted my self-directed, vestibular rehabilitation programme. Visual tracking, which involved holding up an index card and following it with my eyes only, as it moved from side to side and diagonally; quick movements of the eyes (known as saccades) from a card in one hand, across to a card in the other; horizontal movements of my head only, keeping the rest of my body still; focusing on my index finger, as I brought it slowly towards my nose, while turning my head from side to side; and moving my head, without stopping, in the direction of three targets at eye level – over the left shoulder, straight ahead, and then over the right shoulder.

Vestibular rehabilitation is a little like hair-of-the-dog treatment. The purpose of the balance exercises was to achieve what is called central compensation of the brain, by intentionally exposing it, again and again, to a variety of movements that provoke dizziness and other symptoms. By doing so, my brain was being forced to work out a way to adapt to the damage, and turn off any error messages. It wasn't going to happen quickly; the average time for central compensation to occur is six to twelve months. 'Walk, walk, walk' had also been handwritten across my discharge papers, and that's exactly what I intended to do.

'As for driving, I'd suggest waiting another week, and then see how you feel,' wrote Dr Gianoli.

I'd found an email waiting for me on my return, checking how my journey had been. He then responded to my questions.

'When you first drive, do so while there is no traffic, and only for a very short trip. Try to keep your head still, and facing straight ahead. What will get you into trouble is quickly turning your head, to look over your shoulder to change lanes. Don't do this. Use your rear and side view mirrors extensively and, above all, err on the side of caution.'

He encouraged me to continue with the exercises, and to walk for twenty to thirty minutes, both twice daily. I also had to keep water out of my ear, and be sure to follow the list of post-surgery precautions for the full six weeks, including no sneezing or nose blowing, no strenuous activity, and no bending or straining which would put pressure on the abdomen or chest. Pressure of that kind gets transmitted to the head, and consequently to the inner ears.

Avoiding strenuous activity was easier said than done in a household with a boisterous dog, a disabled child, and a renal patient. Hugh's parents had been staying while I was in America, and had left a well-stocked fridge, and home-cooked meals, to tide us over when they departed. My mother arrived shortly afterwards to offer her assistance, but perhaps most of all to keep her eye on me in the recovery period. What my family, and my mother in particular, really wanted to know was had the American operation worked? It was this subject that I started to discuss more extensively with my surgeon.

Robert Klitzman, in his book *When Doctors Become Patients*, discusses the all too common situation whereby patients start to feel disempowered, acting 'as patients, not equals.' This can sometimes be perpetuated by the patients' own reticence. With improved communication, however, and a doctor providing more time and attention, everyone benefits. In the book, it is exemplified in Deborah's approach, a psychiatrist who had also become a cancer patient. 'I'm much more likely to explain why

I'm doing things. Other physicians make decisions, but don't say what they're thinking about to patients. I give my rationale, my doubts.' From the early days of August, I began regular correspondence with Dr Gianoli about the state of my health, and the remaining symptoms. I was never made to feel anything less than an equal. He was a master of communication, and always responded quickly and clearly, and perhaps most importantly, supportively.

My good news was despatched first. The nausea was considerably reduced, and no situation had yet provoked vertigo. My balance was pretty good, my hearing was slowly improving, and all the strange, and often loud, noises in the ear were settling down.

'As regards the fluid', I wrote, 'I'm afraid that's still coming through, although nothing like the quantity it was before the surgery. I'm ninety-nine percent certain at the moment that there must still be a little CSF leak somewhere that is coming and going. I now know how it should feel when it isn't coming through, as I woke up this morning and my head felt great, no pressure, and no fluid wanting to be suctioned out. After a few hours of being up and about, the pressure started to build in my left ear and there were a lot of clunking noises going on, with my ear wanting to pop, and not being able to; I can now feel just little bits of fluid wanting to get out. If I leave this to build up, I know I'll soon get to the point where I badly need to lie down to rest my head, and stop the headache that is growing. On several occasions I've had some really nasty headaches round the back of my head, with sharp, stabbing pains – the only way to relieve them is to keep very still, and let everything settle down.'

I mentioned the link to changeable, low-pressure weather that seemed to have a dramatic effect on my head.

Cerebrospinal fluid (CSF) consists of ninety-nine percent water. The remaining one percent is a mixture of electrolytes, glucose, amino acids and various proteins. At any given time, approximately 90-150 millilitres of it are circulating throughout the central nervous system. Its circulation is maintained by the balance of its production (about twenty millilitres an hour), and its rate of absorption. If elevated intracranial pressure inside the skull develops at any point, as a result of abnormal CSF pressure, there is an increased risk of thinning and weakening of the bone, and the possibility of a defect forming. Diuretic agents, called water pills by some, are able to reduce the water content, and in doing so can decrease the intracranial pressure inside the skull. Hence the reason Dr Gianoli now prescribed the drug Diamox, adding a gentle warning about some common side effects of numbness and tingling in the hands and feet, taste changes, and fatigue.

'All of these tend to get better over time,' he said. 'So if you do have them, and they are tolerable, hang in there.'

He was obviously a doctor that was mindful when prescribing medications, but that could by no means be relied upon, as Robert Klitzman illustrates in his book. It was only when the doctors became ill themselves that they began to view symptoms in a completely new light. 'It's so much easier to understand what a patient is saying. Instead of just discounting "my feet tingle," you truly understand that. I try to frame it to medical students so they can understand. Remember your worst hangover. That's what you're doing to people with these medications – headaches, nausea, vomiting, diarrohea.'

I was about to get a flavour of that worst hangover.

'It's now been over two weeks, and the Diamox is making me feel absolutely terrible,' I moaned, in response to my doctor's enquiry.

'I have a dry mouth the whole time, no matter how much fluid I take in (and it's a lot), and the inside of my mouth feels like sandpaper. The tingling I get in my hands and feet also seems to affect my mouth. The thing is, tingling makes it sound not too unpleasant, but in my case it's really, really bad, and I have it without much relief throughout the day. The feeling is much worse than pins and needles, and it makes the skin on my hands wrinkle up, as though I've been sitting in a bath for hours.

On top of that, the nausea has come back with a vengeance. The tiredness isn't quite as extreme as it was in the first few days, but I still feel totally lacking in energy all the time, and I can't get through the day without a sleep. I don't think I'm imagining it, it also seems to make my mind tired, and in conversations I often struggle to find the right words, or I take much longer to say something. It's having a very bad effect on me.'

Dr Gianoli's response was music to my ears – a cliché, but an appropriate one in the circumstances.

'I am so sorry to hear what a tough time you've had with the Diamox. I think we need to either stop it, or reduce the dose…do not suffer in silence. We'll figure something out. We don't want the treatment to be worse than the disease.'

A week later we stopped it. Another drug, the diuretic Dyazide, was tried, and then another, the antihistamine Tavist, neither with any noticeable benefits, but some unpleasant accompaniments. By mid September, the time was approaching to consider another CT scan, to determine whether there was a failure of the surgical repair, a persistent defect that had not yet been repaired sufficiently, or a CSF leak from another site – one that hadn't yet been identified.

Dr Gianoli already knew from my scans that I had a very holey temporal bone on the left side of my head, one resembling a slab of Swiss cheese. In everyone, there is a thin layer of bone that forms the roof of the middle ear cavity, and separates it from the cranial cavity – the space inside the skull, where the brain resides. The tegmen is the roof's medical name. One of the many nuggets of information I gleaned from Dr Gianoli was that, in roughly eighty percent of SCDS patients, radiology had shown a tegmen with multiple defects, forming a honeycomb pattern. Mine was certainly riddled with holes.

What goes on inside the tunnel of an MRI machine, and the doughnut-shaped hole of a CT scanner, is quite different. The radio-frequency waves from the MRI are best suited for soft tissues, spinal cord injuries, and brain tumours, among other things. The CT emits a multitude of x-ray beams, as it moves through an arc taking numerous pictures, and is better at studying muscle or bone, diagnosing lung and chest problems, and detecting cancers. A CT scan is quicker and quieter, a huge advantage as far as my holey head was concerned, but I had already undergone six of them. A single CT scan exposes the body to between 150 and 1,100 times the amount of radiation of a conventional x-ray, and according to the magazine *Scientific American* that is equivalent to around a year's worth of radiation exposure from natural and artificial sources in the environment. Moreover, a couple of them put a person close to the dose required to cause radiation-induced cataracts. A sobering thought, as I approached my seventh.

The question of whether CT scans increased the risk of cancer had been worrying medical professionals during the four decades of their regular use. However, the studies undertaken to evaluate the risk had been largely based on data from approximately 120,000 survivors of atomic bomb blasts in World War II, and there was a fundamental flaw which made accurate comparisons unlikely. Atomic bombs involve one large blast of gamma rays to a person's entire body, whereas a patient, like me, might have multiple CT scans that concentrated x-rays on just one region of the body. The collected data had suggested a tiny increased risk, of 0.05 percent, of developing a fatal tumour as a result of a single CT scan. In the last few years, however, a group of studies have been underway, examining the rates of various cancers following directly from CT scans. In the meantime, researchers continue to investigate whether effective scanning images can be produced, with lower doses of radiation being discharged. Sarahbjeet Singh, a radiologist at Massachusetts General Hospital, has carried out important research in this field using dead bodies, and has demonstrated that clear diagnoses can be achieved for certain conditions, with seventy-five percent less radiation. Because of the risk of cataracts, in some facilities the scanners will only do coronal slices which avoid the eyes. Reconstructions are then created in other planes.

Any radiation is harmful, that much is sure, but further close examination was needed of my temporal bone, the bone that sits at the sides and base of the skull. Dr Gianoli emailed me the specification details, and I passed them to my GP, knowing there would now most likely be rather a long wait.

Not long after I returned from my American trip, I sat down to write some important letters. My overriding motivation was that other patients in the future, particularly those with SCDS, should not hit the brick walls that I had so frequently found myself bashing my head against. At this early stage it wasn't easy to use a computer, as taking my eyes from the screen, and then back up again, made me feel as though I was falling over, even though I was sitting down. I had to build it up gradually.

To the consultant whose sole remedy suggestion had been a lesson in symptom management, I explained why I found his approach patronising, and insulting. To the hospital emergency department, I explained the importance of understanding the link between panic attacks and vestibular disorders. To the Oxford consultant who had diagnosed me, and made the referral to my surgeon, I explained how I had been forced to cross the Atlantic for revision surgery. To the House of Hearing, whose audiologist had recommended a doctor who considered my ability to sit through a consultation an indication that nothing much was wrong with me, I suggested that such a recommendation should never be repeated. And to Professor Lello (doctor no.8), who had done his utmost to help and support me, a different letter, one of appreciation. He responded promptly, with his usual courtesy.

'Thank you for having taken the time and trouble to write to me. It must have been the faith and conviction that you had in being right in the description of your symptoms that carried you through, and congratulations in persevering where so many of us in the medical profession fell short. It is with great pleasure that I am now able to take your clinical notes, which I have been carrying in my work briefcase for this past year, and file them away, in the expectation that you will make the full recovery you so richly deserve.'

I hadn't the heart to tell him it might be a little too soon for that.

I also had some homework to get stuck into – how to instigate a formal complaint against an NHS Hospital Trust. My mother had paid a very substantial amount of money for me to travel abroad for medical treatment, I now had a comprehensive surgery report detailing everything that had needed to be done, and I felt it was my responsibility to try to obtain financial compensation for her. My father had been at pains to leave my mother financially well provided for, but she was now reaching the last stage of her life, and no-one knew how much care she might need herself at some point. The complaint process was going to take time and effort on my part, and that, coupled with the fact that I still had health complications, persuaded me to abandon self-employment on my local business directory. It was a blow. I'd been gradually building up a circle of regular customers, I was enjoying the creative aspects of designing advertisements, and writing articles and restaurant reviews, and I had hoped to expand the business with an online website. But something had to give. The likelihood was that the official complaint would escalate to become a legal claim, and I had to be able devote hours and hours to gathering all the evidence, and presenting a convincing case. I set the wheels in motion, by exercising my right of access to all my medical records, which as usual involved a payment for administrative costs – every last piece of paper and CD that had recorded notes, tests, correspondence and scans.

It was at this point that a disturbing fact emerged from some correspondence that had passed between two of my consultants, in the year of my diagnosis. Mr Bradford (doctor no.3) who first identified my condition as SCDS, and Mr Ingram (doctor no.4) who subsequently performed surgery, were, I discovered, both aware that my 2006-7 scans had shown thin bone on the right side of my head. Neither had thought to disclose this fact, or discuss it with me. I was only told about the hole on the left.

Infuriated by this withholding of information, I looked up the guidance for doctors, with regard to the copying of letters to patients. I found that, despite the strong support for the practice among health bodies, and an encouragement for doctors to use plain and simple language, there was no contractual obligation for a letter to be copied. I was dismayed by this. I had already had to draw Mr Bradford's attention to an incorrect and misleading statement within a letter he had sent to my GP, but this was far more serious – it directly related to my diagnosis, or incomplete diagnosis as it turned out to be. (The later CT scan, specified by Dr Gianoli, had shown without doubt a hole on the right side, not just thin bone.) I couldn't comprehend why two doctors should be allowed to share knowledge about significant structural abnormalities inside my head, and yet I, the owner of that head, could be kept in the dark.

It wasn't until some months later that I realised the full implication of this concealment, when I became aware that symptoms typical of SCDS can occur in cases where there is thin bone, but no actual hole. Dr Gianoli had been aware of this fact for years, but in 2013 a study was published that underscored it. It was authored by Dr Minor, among others – the man who first identified the syndrome – and revealed the results of ten cases falling into this category. All ten patients' symptoms had improved post-operatively. It is also now generally recognised that in a patient with one ear symptomatic and a hole, the other ear has less than normal bone thickness. And about fifty percent of the time, the other ear has an actual hole too.

On October 30, nearly four months after my operation, I was back in a CT scanner. This time the main obstacle proved to be finding someone capable of understanding what the resulting images showed. I had made sure I obtained a CD that I could post to Dr Gianoli in Louisiana, but there would be a delay before he received and reviewed it, particularly with the holiday period of Thanksgiving coming up. The cursory scan report that made its way to my GP was completely meaningless, so I tracked down the consultant neuroradiologist that had reviewed earlier scans, and therefore had the relevant expertise and context with which to make sense of this one.

The wait made me feel ill at ease. So much was hanging in the balance. If nothing showed up, I'd have no explanation for my continued fluid symptoms, but if a problem was located, my surgeon was thousands of miles away, so what would I do?

'There's no sign of fluid within the middle ear, or in the back of your throat,' wrote the radiologist in his email. 'But there is a tiny defect in the left temporal bone, towards the front, and a small bubble or two of gas, which may represent a site of communication between the ear and the intracranial space.' In other words, he had found a possible hole, and where there's a hole, there's potential for a leak.

'The radiologist's finding may be a big clue,' replied Dr Gianoli, when I passed on this information. 'I would definitely like to scrutinise that area.' But my CD still hadn't arrived, and when it eventually did on December 9, there were technical problems getting it to open up.

'The repair site looks good.' At last Dr Gianoli could see the images.

'But there's an area just in front of the repair (ie. not repaired) that looks suspicious. Perhaps this is the area the radiologist discussed with you?'

By now I was a bundle of nerves. I'd recently received some stark news from Patrick's spinal consultant which had added a new, and alarming, dimension to our family complications. On the one hand I badly wanted to know the reason for my recurrent head symptoms, on the other hand considerable anxiety was provoked, by pondering how and where a solution to it was going to be found.

'We should talk. When would be a good time to call?' Dr Gianoli asked.

Scotland is six hours ahead of Louisiana, so we spoke early that evening. The conversation was rather stilted because of the echo and time delay, and I had to be sure I understood exactly what my surgeon was telling me. He seemed to be saying that he considered his job incomplete. He needed to open up my head a second time, and if I could get myself back over there fairly soon, he would finish what he'd started. He explained what he would do in the operation, and apologised for the fact that the hospital charge, as opposed to his surgery fee, was out of his control. His sentiments were so far removed from the conversations with my first surgeon that I was worried I'd misunderstood.

Shortly after we'd finished speaking, I wrote to him.

'I just want to let you know how grateful I am for your very kind offer to waive your fee for my surgery. As I said to you on the phone, I very much want you to be the doctor that I see again, but of course the costs are a huge factor, and your offer makes an enormous difference. I had very bad news about my son a week ago. He has to have dangerous surgery in 2010 to correct a curvature of the spine, and I had to discuss it with the surgeon, without even knowing what was still wrong with my head, and how I would ever get it fixed. You have given me the best possible Christmas present. Thank you.'

'You are most welcome,' he replied. 'You are a good person, who's had her share of misfortune. You deserve something good to happen to you. Merry Christmas!'

16

SIGN OF MADNESS

It was becoming ever more important to find a legal firm that would pursue a compensation claim against the NHS Hospital Trust, as my mother insisted on funding the return trip to America. I wasn't in a position to turn down her offer; I just had to step up my efforts for her to be repaid. Letters had been going back and forth between me and the trust as part of the complaint process, but I was making no headway in terms of them accepting liability for their failings. Round in circles we went.

I received an exciting phone call, the day before leaving for Louisiana. I had contacted several companies to find out whether they would consider my case on a 'no win, no fee' basis, but so far all had declined. There was a case to answer, they all assured me after examining the correspondence, but it was an extremely complex one, and they weren't prepared to take on the challenge. Fourth time lucky, the phone call proved to be. The lawyer was willing to act on my behalf, and wasn't put off when I told him I was about to return for another operation.

Holidays did not seem to feature very prominently in the life of my busy neuro-otologist, but Mardi Gras (French for fat Tuesday), with its vibrant parades through the streets of New Orleans, was a day kept clear in Dr Gianoli's annual work calendar. Louisiana had declared it a legal state holiday back in

1875, and it could fall on any Tuesday between the beginning of February and March. In 2010, it was the week bang in the middle, so February 25 was the day we scheduled for my revision craniotomy. This date could also be fitted in around my sister's social work job, managing a team who cared for acutely ill, elderly people at home, to prevent their admission into hospital.

My faithful nurse still at my side, we installed ourselves in the same hotel, the only difference being that this time we agreed it made sense to make better use of the on site catering, as an evening buffet was provided, with no additional charge, during the week. My only knowledge of the local cuisine to date was limited to the lyrics of a Carpenters' song, in which Jamabalaya, crawfish pie and fillet gumbo are mentioned. The evening menus in fact turned out to range ambitiously across continents, but nevertheless salty, deep-fried beans, rice, corn, chicken, pork and spicy sauces regularly made their appearance.

I steered well clear of Ibuprofen, we switched off car headlights assiduously, and I sailed through the second opening up of my skull. When my surgeon visited me on Saturday morning, the day of discharge, I was in a private room all alone.

'Good morning, how are you? You're looking great.' His approach was cheery and positive as usual.

'Thank you. Yes, I'm feeling fine, and I was very hungry when they brought my breakfast,' I said. 'But one thing I know for sure is I'm not looking great – I've just been to the bathroom, and caught a glimpse in the mirror.'

Moments before Dr Gianoli had entered the room I'd disentangled the leads on the drip stand, and carefully manoeuvred myself up off the bed. The lop-sided turban bandage was familiar, but this time several brownish-green bruises on my sallow skin gave my face the appearance of a damaged peach, and the dark circles around my blue-grey eyes glowered at me.

The surgeon had moved round to the far side of my bed, and sat down on the chair by the large window. Within those few seconds, weariness seemed to have swept over him, and he looked intensely at me, deep concern in his gaze. He took off his glasses, rubbed his eyes, and then replaced them.

'I found several more holes, and they're all filled in now. It was fascinating actually, seeing inside your head relatively soon after the last operation. I took a picture, as I don't usually get an opportunity to do that with patients. Almost all the cement paste had turned to bone. It's looking good.'

He hesitated. It was clear there was more to tell me, and he was reluctant to release the words.

'I'm afraid there was no CSF leak. And so from that point of view, we're no further forward.'

He looked lost in thought for a moment, but the sight of my crestfallen face appeared to jolt him back into conversation.

'I presume you have someone over here with you? Are they coming to collect you today?'

I nodded, and replied that my sister was probably on her way.

'I think you should return to your hotel, rest for a day or so, and let's wait and see how your head is, and whether you think there's still fluid getting through. You can contact me on my cell phone – you've got the number, haven't you?'

I felt queasy with dismay. 'And what if I think there is?' I asked. 'What do we do then?'

'There's really only one thing we can do – a radionuclide cisternogram to look for the leak. It would be slightly different to what you had done a while ago, back home. I'd need to have you come to the office on Tuesday, and I'd set things up to cover the few days before you fly home.'

I was tense and irritable in our rooms in Baton Rouge, although I was trying hard not to let my gloom create an un-pleasant atmosphere. By Sunday morning I was sure that the problem in my head hadn't resolved. It was a beautiful, warm and breezy spring day outside, and I was relieved when at last Georgie agreed to leave me for a few hours to visit the Magno-lia Mound Plantation, an 18th-century French Creole house near the river, a short drive away. On her return, she tried to cheer me up, describing the well-preserved slave quarters and overseer's house, and the elderly, pony-tailed guide who had escorted the small group of visitors from room to room, rounding things off in the old kitchen with a demonstration of how to break up lumps of sugar cane. While she heated up some water for us both to have a cup of tea, I told her my mind was made up. I was going to text Dr Gianoli, as we needed to proceed with the leak search.

It wasn't until I was in the examination chair in the Ear and Balance Institute, my sister watching from across the room, that the undignified nature of the new investigation began to emerge. Doctor Gianoli was in playful mode. While he joked that having a second lumbar puncture was a sign of madness (and I hadn't even had a chance to fully enlighten him about the full horror of the first), he was busy shovelling small wads of absorbent material up my nostrils. The nasal intruders, known as pledgets in the medical world, had to remain in position for a couple of days. I wanted to yank them out after about ten minutes – how was I going to tolerate that length of time? While completing his handiwork, taping little pieces of rubber tubing in place across my cheeks, he began regaling us with an amusing nostril story from his younger days. Georgie was enjoying the entertainment, but I was forced to raise my hand to bring it to a halt, as the wads were at high risk of being snorted out with laughter. It would have been ironic in the circumstances, as the tale involved a particularly disagreeable male patient who had done exactly that, pledgets and much more besides, but with full intention.

We were sent on our way, Georgie clutching directions to take us to the torture facility. The one in which I was to be subjected to the lumbar puncture, with a tracer injected into my spinal fluid. My vow a year and a half earlier, never to put myself through another one of these procedures, was at the forefront of my mind, but I could see no alternative if we were ever to locate the source of the problem. The tracer would spread up the spinal column and into my brain, and the progress of it would be recorded by a nuclear medicine gamma camera, which thankfully involved very little radiation. Images were going to be taken at four hours and twenty four hours, and the six pledgets would also be examined for evidence at the end of the process.

Those first four hours had to be spent on the premises, lying flat on a hard bed in a small, airless room, sipping water through a straw to stave off a debilitating headache, but unable to get up to walk around, or empty my bladder. We were very ill-prepared for the session, no means of watching a film to while away the hours, not even an iPod with some distracting music. There was a large clock on the wall at the end of the bed, so my choices were limited to watching the red second hand jerk its way laboriously round and round in circles, or closing my eyes to drift away on a cushioned raft, the waves of a clear, azure sea gently rippling at its edges. After the first couple of hours had crawled by, the desire to get up, stretch my legs and pay a visit to the toilet, imbedded itself within my brain, and every minute became a battle to resist the urges. By that point, dreaming of any sort of water only made matters worse.

Patients with CSF leaks present a diagnostic challenge to both clinicians and radiologists. There are various combinations of scanning and injections of contrast agents that can be tried, to show up the leak, but none of them are foolproof or totally successful, partly because most leaks are intermittent. The use of the pledgets is designed to increase the chance of finding the leak. It is not unusual for a CSF leak to spontaneously resolve by itself, but in my case this clearly hadn't happened as so much time had passed. It is important to find it because, if left untreated, it may result in recurrent meningitis.

By the time we returned to Dr Gianoli's office on Thursday, the scanning was complete, the pledgets had been removed, but I hadn't been given any information about what the whole ghastly procedure had revealed. The answer turned out to be, quite simply, nothing. Yet again, no sign of escaping brain fluid had been found. My symptoms remained a mystery.

The mood in the consulting room was sombre, while I discussed with Dr Gianoli what should be done now. My surgeon was flummoxed, as we all were, but he suggested that he put a ventilation tube in my eardrum right there and then, in the hope that it might at least partially help relieve some of my symptoms. I made a mental note that precisely what he was doing, without inflicting any pain and within a matter of minutes while I remained in the examination chair, Mr Scott (doctor no.10) had suggested I spend £1500 for him to do, under general anaesthetic on an operating table.

It was time to say goodbye. I was leaving with another handy scopolamine patch to be applied for the journey home, as well as a very heavy heart. Dr Gianoli hugged me as we stood up to go, and within seconds my body was convulsing with sobs, as the tears pushed their way to the surface. I was overcome with emotion. Stress from the major operation, quickly followed by the lengthy and invasive procedure amounting to nothing, caught up with me in that hug. Dr Gianoli released himself, left the room abruptly, and my sister escorted me out of the building, tears still seeping out. I must have looked a pitiful sight when Val rushed out into the corridor, pointing out that we were holding all the notes that should have been handed over to her at the desk. She was concerned to see me crying, and another embrace was wrapped around me.

I knew I had to pull myself together for the flight home the next day. I was fully aware this time that a crippling headache, following on from the nuclear scan test, was a distinct possibility and, to ensure I staved it off, I had been drinking plenty of water, and putting my feet up as often as I could. This had so far been keeping severe pain at bay. The long-haul, overnight part of the journey, from Friday evening to Saturday morning, was the period I was silently dreading, and my worst fears were founded long before we approached London Heathrow. By the time the bright lights were switched back on by the cabin staff, and a lukewarm breakfast, on its plastic tray, had crash landed onto my fold-down table, I knew I had serious trouble on my hands. It was a toss up between compelling myself to nibble on something from within the slightly moist, cellophane package, to allay Georgie's suspicions, and confessing that the discomfort, from hours spent with my legs twisted or my knees jammed against the seat back, was now out of my control, and had reached throwing up proportions.

'Aren't you hungry?' said Georgie, eyeing me sternly over the top of her reading glasses.

'Not really,' I said, as I tentatively began to peel the banana, having decided it looked the least offensive member of the breakfast offerings. I took a tiny sip from my plastic cup of tea, but it prompted me to lunge for the paper sick bag that was tucked inside the netting pocket. I needed it very close at hand.

'Are you going to be sick, Philippa?' Adding my name injected a censorious tone to the enquiry, as it so often does, curiously enough. My sister's face had turned slightly grey, and she stared hard at me, her body stiff and upright, as though primed to make a run for it.

'I don't think so,' I said. 'I'm trying to get it under control, but it means I can't talk to you. I feel really dreadful. I'm going to have to stay here in my seat once we've landed, and let everyone else get off first. I've been in agony because of that bloody lumbar puncture.'

The process, as an aircraft slowly taxis into its gate at the terminal, and the passengers then gather up their belongings and shuffle off at a snail's pace, is always a frustratingly slow one, but on this occasion it seemed interminable. I slunk down into my window corner out of sight, unfastened the seat belt, and took a series of very deep breaths, while pressing my clammy fingers into my forehead in repetitive circular movements, attempting to alleviate the excruciating head pain and intense nausea. I instinctively knew I would feel immeasurably better if I could vomit into the bag, but at such close proximity to my sister, it wasn't an option.

Once the plane had emptied, I stumbled along the aisle to the exit door, Georgie following close behind me. Sitting in my wheelchair, I managed to make it all the way out to the airport arrivals area, where my brother-in-law was waiting to help us out to his parked car. I was still barely able to communicate verbally. I was using all my powers of concentration to contain the situation, and as soon as I had sat down in the back of the car, and there was sufficient distance between me and my phobic sister, I could contain it no longer. I was sick, superlatively so. The unpleasant incident fortunately occurred before either Georgie or her husband had got into the car, as they were still conversing outside it, and even more fortunately, an empty plastic bag was within my reach. Henry kindly disposed of the bag, no longer an empty one. The relief was immense, and I spent the car journey to their home in Suffolk stretched out along the back seat, in relative contentment. I wasn't offered any nourishment, not that I would have accepted any.

After a further lengthy sit from Suffolk all the way up to Scotland on the train the next day, I arrived home again at last. It had been another absence of nearly two weeks, and it was deeply depressing to think that the costly trip had been largely in vain. The scopolamine patch hadn't managed to prevent sickness this time, but for the first few days my head didn't seem to be filling up with liquid at the same rate as it usually did, so I was thankful for small mercies. For as long as I could remember, in times of trouble my natural instinct was to read, research, and learn – information equalled control. I therefore spent every spare minute exploring the internet again, searching for pointers that could help direct the next step forward. There had to be an explanation for the fluid. I was looking for anything, however tiny, that might provide the vital clue that had been overlooked.

In an email to Dr Gianoli, I mentioned the very dark vein running across the lower part of my left cheek. An acupuncturist, whom I had been visiting in Edinburgh before my first American operation, had remarked on the fact that it appeared to be engorged, and more than one friend had commented on it, assuming I had an ink stain, or a smear of something that I needed to wipe off my face.

'According to the Monroe-Kellie hypothesis, about vascular dilatation compensating for reduced CSF volume,' I wrote, 'it has been proven that, in some cases, engorgement of spinal, epidural veins can cause nerve compression.'

I knew that with no medical background, and a limited understanding of the complicated terminology that was often involved, I could be widely off the mark, but I'd just been reading an article which suggested that the pain in my thumb and forefinger (as described to the radiologist in Manchester) could be a significant symptom, and the engorged vein on my face might be linked to it.

'There is downward displacement of venous blood,' I continued with my potentially nonsensical theory. 'Sometimes the exiting nerve roots are compressed. The person described in the article had a spinal leak, but cranial leaks were also mentioned. The case study also confirmed that it's not unusual to have a normal looking head MRI, which I've had, because the typical features of the leak are only seen in repeat MRI scans, or sometimes never at all.'

I remained convinced that there must be a CSF leak somewhere, and it simply hadn't been found yet. I was, in fact, clinging to this belief, because without it I might as well wave goodbye to any hope of getting better. Judging by the enthusiastic response, my wild speculations seemed to help steer Dr Gianoli's train of thought too.

'Wow, I am truly impressed,' he wrote back. 'Everything you have told me makes lots of sense. The only problem is it doesn't help localise the leak. What you've stated is true, regardless of the location. I think we have to consider another location.'

It was a relief to know we hadn't yet exhausted all lines of enquiry, and I was further reassured when he informed me that he was going to carefully re-examine every single one of my scans, to see if he had missed something. It wasn't long afterwards, at the end of March, Dr Gianoli concluded that on not one of them could he see a full, unimpeded view of my sinuses. It was time, we agreed, for the eighth CT scan, one that would focus on that particular region of my problematic head.

Dr Gianoli was exceeding all hopes I'd had of finding a dedicated and thorough doctor to help me, and I wanted him to know how much I appreciated everything he was doing, including all the extra time and effort he had contributed during our recent stay in Louisiana. It took a little while to work out the best way to show this appreciation, but I settled on a surprise food hamper. I planned to fill it with some of the finest, local Scottish products. The postage in fact ended up costing as much as the contents, because of the weight, but I was pleased with the idea of sending items that couldn't easily be bought in his part of the world, and which the doctor and his family had probably never sampled before. A few miles from home, in the traditional, old village of Tyninghame, I'd located a specialist store that prepared beautifully made gift hampers. I paid them a visit, to personally select a range of cheeses, chutneys, jams, oatcakes and a few sweet treats, carefully avoiding items that I'd discovered were on the Food and Drug Administration's highly restricted list for export to the States. The owners of the store were intrigued to hear about the gift's faraway destination, and its worthy recipient.

Once that was in hand, I drove back up the road a short distance, and took a right turn to head towards John Muir Country Park, named after the famous Scottish-American conservationist whose birthplace was nearby, in the coastal town of Dunbar. Maisie, our spaniel, leaped out of the car and we spent an enjoyable half an hour wandering along the paths in the pine woods, and out onto the open area of grassland overlooking the large salt marsh. Just as we approached the last bend on our return to the car, with a streak of black and grey she was gone. She had dashed into some rhododendron bushes, and failed to reappear, despite my repeated calls. The likelihood was that she had caught the scent of a pheasant, and was on its trail. Getting home, to relieve the pressure from liquid in my head, was now a priority, and my patience was wearing thin. Deciding to replicate the behaviour of an over-excited cocker spaniel, I crawled my way through the bushes, and came out into an enormous barley field, beyond which was an enticing copse – it looked a perfect spot for a dog wanting a good rummage. I zigzagged my way through the spiky crop, which was nearly up to my knees, and started shouting again, as I scoured the bracken on the far side. For over an hour I searched and called, to no avail.

Now I was sincerely worried. The park spans an area of over seven square kilometres. I couldn't possibly search it all. I was hot and bothered; it was a warm afternoon, and I peeled off my jacket. As I did so, an extremely faint, whimpering noise wafted across on the breeze. I stood still, and strained to hear it, but my imperfect ears, and the swaying trees with their rustling leaves, stymied my attempts. The whimper reached me again, but it now seemed to be coming from an altogether different direction. It was hopeless. I pulled my phone out of the pocket of my jeans.

'Amy, I'm coming to get you. I'll probably be there in about twenty minutes. We'll have to drive back here, and comb this area together, inch by inch. She's here somewhere, I'm sure I heard her, but I just can't find her.'

We sped back along the winding road, and Amy wanted to know what we'd do if we couldn't locate our pet quickly. Patrick would be dropped home from his special needs unit soon, so we had a limited time frame in which to work. We battled our way through some overgrown shrubs at the side of the path, and staggered out into the vast field. The full scale of the problem then became evident to my daughter. We started making our way back across the knee-high barley, trampling a path as we went, and scanning the countryside all around us. More than halfway across, my eyes dropped to my feet, and I veered a little to the right as I carried on walking. The move proved to be uncanny in its accuracy. I'll never know why I suddenly chose to do that. I nearly fell into it myself – a deep, narrow hole in the ground, completely concealed by the tall cereal grain growing all around it. Two anxious, dark eyes stared up at me, and a black nose that was covered in earth. I got down on my knees, and hauled Maisie out, her paws caked in dried soil from failed attempts to scramble out of her underground cell.

My heart was brimming with relief and love for the dirty animal. I hugged her, and stroked her, again and again. We'd brought water with us, and gave her a drink from the fold-away bowl. During the return drive to our house, it was distressing to contemplate the alternative outcome, which would surely have been eventual death by starvation, or dehydration, unable to escape on her own, and no-one to hear her feeble whines in such a remote setting. I would never have been able to forgive myself, if we'd had to go home without her. And the truth was, I also needed her. She may have been just a dog, but she was a vital part of my support system.

17

DEVIL'S BREATH

'Please do not get depressed. I'm not giving up on your case, regardless of whether you have a CSF leak or not.'

Dr Gianoli could apparently read minds, even from thousands of miles away.

His words gave me enormous relief. I read them again five years later, and they produced an instantaneous and unexpected result. The floodgates opened, and I dissolved into tears. I had buried the past anguish very deep inside me, but my memory of how I reacted at the time was vivid. The biochemist Dr William Frey would no doubt have found the tears contained a high level of protein-based hormones. He has conducted a study of crying, and concluded that emotional tears of that kind help to wash chemicals linked to stress out of the body. Deep crying exposes deep feelings, and they can then be dealt with rather than being left to fester, causing physical and psychological damage. In May 2010, it was extraordinarily important to me that I wasn't abandoned. I still had something mysteriously wrong on one side of my head, and I also knew now that I had a hole on the other – we hadn't even begun to discuss what trouble that might cause me. I had been left high and dry by my first surgeon, and it was absolutely crucial to me that it didn't happen again. What was never out of my mind was the depth to which I had sunk the first time.

Early in May, the package containing a CD of the scan set out on its long voyage. The first hold up was caused by an enormous ash cloud spreading out from a volcanic eruption in Iceland, and then it had to traverse oily seas, resulting from the Deepwater Horizon rig explosion. In April, millions of barrels of oil had been dumped into the Gulf of Mexico. The scan reached Louisiana just three weeks before hurricane season was due to start. But it was a wasted journey – the images produced nothing of any note.

'I went over things with a fine tooth comb this morning,' Dr Gianoli wrote. 'There are some areas of either very thin bone or possible dehiscence, but there is no sign of any soft tissue herniation, or fluid accumulation. The only possible spot in my mind for a CSF leak (and I even think this is unlikely) is near the Eustachian tube.'

Dr Gianoli's conclusions more or less matched those of the British radiologist, but he had an advantage, as he pointed out – 'I have the luxury of knowing what things look like inside your head.'

I answered a number of questions the doctor put to me, and I also went round and round in circles reading about the routes of different nerves, and where they might be compressed, trying to give him a new line of investigation. It didn't get me very far, as I told him.

'I've tried looking at the problem in reverse, by considering what helps relieve the pain and pressure, apart from suctioning out fluid. If I bend my head far down over my knees, that's good; lying down, and tipping my head back as far as it will go, helps the headaches, and removes all the pressure around my ear; yawning, or opening my mouth really wide, brings relief too. I think I should just live like a bat, hanging from the ceiling – that's the answer.'

'Yes,' wrote Dr Gianoli. 'You have so many symptoms consistent with a CSF leak, but not quite enough hard findings to make the diagnosis.'

Orthostatic, or positional, headaches are generally accepted as a possible consequence following a diagnostic lumbar puncture (I could now personally vouch for that), but are not well recognised outside that context. A headache that occurs shortly after assuming an upright position, and is relieved by lying down, is one of the prototypical signs of a CSF leak. I had been having them regularly.

In the midst of our correspondence I mentioned a different symptom, one that hadn't been talked about before. It was to prove one of the linchpins in the solving of my head puzzle, and highlighted how much every tiny detail matters, when a patient describes their condition. Insufficient time had so frequently been a problem in my medical consultations, and I had also become worn down by the doctors in Britain ignoring, or only half listening to, the information I was giving them. I lost faith in my own judgment about what might be significant.

'On many occasions, most noticeably evenings when I've had what felt like buckets of runny liquid pouring down through my head, some of it has escaped out of the bottom corner of my left eye,' I explained, 'and I definitely wasn't crying when it happened. It was as though the liquid was looking for any way out that it could find. I haven't noticed it as significantly since the first operation with you, but I know it still happens. I've read that CSF can sometimes escape in that way. Is that correct?'

I had decided to bring this up, as recalling a past incident with Patrick made me wonder whether he had caused some damage to the fragile structure of my head. Dr Gianoli had already been informed of the occasion on which my son had brought the heavy bath handrail crashing down onto my head, but he didn't know of this earlier assault. People didn't tend to realise how hazardous it could be, caring for a child with complex special needs. Patrick enjoyed standing up, and swinging himself back and forth, while using my hands as his support.

We were in the hall enjoying this game, when my daughter came in through the front door. I took my eye off the rocking boy for a few seconds to greet Amy, and wham – he hit me with the full force of his hard head just below the left eye. It was around the time of this event that a very big, jelly-like floater developed in the centre of the visual axis of the same eye, but none of the ophthalmologists could fathom why someone of my age should have developed such a monstrous specimen.

While Dr Gianoli carefully evaluated the implications of everything I was telling him, I began hatching a new plan.

There was a watery substance that sometimes ran out of my eye; I still regularly found it escaping in little trickles from my nose, particularly while out walking the dog; I remained like a barometer, with my worst symptoms during low pressure, changeable weather days; a large amount of my time, each day without fail, was spent simply removing this substance from my head; and to top it all, Patrick was slowly working his way up an NHS waiting list, getting closer to the dangerous all-day spinal surgery. I had no idea how I was going to be able to deal with many months of intensively nursing him back to full health, while I was in such a hopeless state myself. My husband's health was also deteriorating, and his blood pressure was far too high. I knew I was clutching at straws, and potentially wasting several hundred pounds, but I decided to arrange another private scan. I'd had years of doing everything the way the British medical system dictated, so I was very familiar with all the rules. This time I intended to break most of them. I would not only make the decision about the need for a scan, but I was going to provide the specification for it myself.

My many months of research into CSF leaks, and a number of emails to specialists abroad (including Dr Timothy Hain in Chicago, where he is known as the Dizzy Doctor) had indicated that a newer test, using MRI (not CT) in a very specific way that would greatly increase any signal from cerebrospinal fluid, had been shown to have a very high success rate. I carefully worded my letter to the GP, to give the impression that my American surgeon and the British radiologist had found the last CT scan insufficient, and that an additional MRI would be beneficial. I hoped he would assume the request came from them, and fortunately he did, happily passing on the necessary referral to the Edinburgh scanning facility.

I then had to ensure that the senior radiologist in charge of the report would be the same one as before, that he would personally compare the two scans, and that the extremely detailed instructions were followed without anyone knowing that they had been compiled by me, someone without medical qualifications. Most of the jargon made limited sense to me, being neither a physician nor a radiologist, but I had found the information in a scholarly online study, and it looked to be just the ticket, as my Aunt Betty used to be fond of saying.

Everything went swimmingly well, and I was horizontal in a scanning tunnel again early in June. It was beyond ridiculous now – perhaps it was time to investigate a timeshare in one. I resisted suctioning fluid out of my head beforehand, as I needed it to be as full of the stuff as possible. The whole procedure took about forty-five minutes, and a severe panic attack was only narrowly avoided as it was such a long time. The radiologist helped me out of the tunnel, commenting on the length of the procedure, and explaining it was because I was having such an incredibly specific type of scan.

'Yes, I know,' I responded, resisting the temptation to boast of my achievement by adding, 'I put the spec together myself. I'm glad it all made sense.'

Once a CD had been despatched to Dr Gianoli, I explained to him that I had managed to proceed with the scanning arrangement without troubling him, and I gave some background to the concerns driving the decision.

'Patrick is nearly fourteen. My son is tall, and getting harder to manage every day. He has no speech, the mental age of about a one-year old, and he needs care in every aspect of his life, twenty-four hours a day. He's a wonderful boy, but extremely challenging. His epilepsy is not at all well controlled at the moment and, as you know, he has to have a very major operation on his back. The spinal surgeon has taken the view that it would be far preferable for me to be fixed before they tackle this, as I shall need to stay in hospital with him for about four weeks, with a much longer recuperation period afterwards at home. I'm obviously still not really better, and they're going to be ready for him in the not too distant future, so there's a big problem looming now.'

Before I wrote the email, I had been urged by Georgie to spell things out to Dr Gianoli. She must have sensed my increasing desperation, and wanted to be sure I conveyed it to my doctor.

'I do have to find a fast solution to the fluid problem, and I realise that may involve taking some decisions that are far from ideal. You've explained that one option would involve a loss of hearing on my left side, but that may be the option I have to take. I honestly can't continue much longer living the way I do at the moment. Absolutely everything has to be planned around this process of emptying my head, and there is not a single minute in the day when I am not thinking about, and managing, this fluid.'

A copy of the scan report arrived in the post, and I skimmed it rapidly looking for good news.

'There is a linear trace of fluid signal, under the margin of the left temporal bone repair.'

I homed in on these words, which amounted to less than a sentence within a page of writing, and chose to block out the important ones in the concluding paragraph which indicated this finding was 'unlikely to be clinically significant.' As far as I was concerned, Dr Summers' report, with the suggestion of a trace of fluid, offered a flicker of hope, and now I had to wait for my American surgeon to express his opinion after studying the scan.

The wait lengthened. DHL decided to redirect my package to PA for Pennsylvania, rather than LA for Louisiana, but at last on June 17, Dr Gianoli confirmed he had received it. Several more days passed before I heard from him again, and then his simple question unnerved me.

'Can I call you tomorrow morning, around 7.30-8.00 am my time?'

I answered in the affirmative, and offered to make the call myself. Not a great deal of sleep was enjoyed that night. The next day another email popped up.

'I'm sorry, but I didn't have any internet access last night. It's actually easier for me to call you, but I'm running late this morning. Can I call you tomorrow instead? As for your situation, I have one more question. How long after the first surgery before the drainage started, and how long after the second? The second I believe was three days or so, but the first I think was one or two weeks – is that correct?'

I was on tenterhooks now. I couldn't work out why he would be asking these questions, but I replied as accurately as I could.

'After both surgeries I had an idea that really small amounts were coming through very soon. In July, when I saw you back in the clinic a week after the surgery, I expressed concern that I could feel a tiny bit. But as you say, it was one or two weeks before the quantity increased, and I was certain I still had a noticeable leak. After the second surgery, I was sure by the Sunday evening, so yes, about three days.'

Dr Gianoli telephoned me at home the next day. The conversation got off to an encouraging start, as he told me he was pleased that I had arranged the latest scan. But the next piece of information was definitely not what I was expecting to hear.

'Yes, I'm glad, as I feel absolutely sure now that you don't have a CSF leak.'

I took a sharp intake of breath, and felt my heart start to beat faster. I began slowly pacing around in a circle while pressing the receiver close to my ear. I didn't want to miss a single word of the doctor's explanation.

He had poured over the scans, and was quite sure there were no signs of a leak. A complicated new term, geniculate ganglion, was introduced. The little nerve centre, situated above the balance canals, apparently had no bony coverage on the left side of my head, whereas on the right it was mostly protected by bone. Whether or not this fact was significant in terms of my symptoms, Dr Gianoli was almost positive that the parasympathetic nerves, passing through that area, were over stimulating all my glands – they had basically gone beserk. It would account for the runny liquid that was appearing in various locations – nasal fluid from the nostril, excessive tearing from the eye, and engorged salivary glands inside my cheek, and below the jaw line.

It was at this point in the conversation that Devil's Breath made its appearance. Scare stories abound of victims forced to inhale the toxic substance, or have it absorbed through their skin, swiftly turning them into zombies who have no recollection of events, as their memories are blocked from forming. It's been rumoured that some have been left unable to speak, and very high doses can certainly be lethal. Of course Dr Gianoli wasn't actually using the name Devil's Breath, and he wasn't suggesting either that I start abusing what has been termed the most dangerous drug in the world, one derived from nightshade plants. He was referring to scopolamine prescribed at a very low dose, in the form of a Transderm Scop patch that had been applied to my neck, on more than one occasion.

The surgeon had ingeniously made a connection between the short periods in which I had relief from the fluid build up, albeit only partially, and the little skin patches of anticholinergic cream – anticholinergic meaning that it inhibits the parasympathetic nerve impulses. Scientists believe that scopolamine prevents communication between the nerves of the vestibular part of the ear and the vomiting centre in the brain, and it achieves this by blocking the action of the chemical that nerves use to transmit messages to each other. Scopolamine is indeed very potent, and can certainly affect the central nervous system, as it readily crosses what's known as the blood-brain barrier – a layer of tightly packed cells which protect the brain from unwanted chemicals. The fact that the patches had given me some respite from my ceaseless torment was a very strong indication that the scopolamine was at work, dampening the effects of the overactive nerves.

'You had one patch placed in the operating room on July 9, the date of your first operation, and then I gave you another to apply on July 16,' said Dr Gianoli. 'So you had two patches within a week's time.'

He was explaining the reason for his questions before the phone call, and how he had gradually made the link. He seemed to be frustrated with himself for having taken so long to work it all out. The doctor wanted me to carry out a trial at home, recording how often I had to pump out the fluid, then applying a patch, and recording the same process again. I was also to buy some sugar free lemon drops, and go through the recording process a third time, sucking two of the drops each hour to help keep the saliva flowing freely, rather than getting engorged.

'Let's see what happens,' he said. 'I've got my fingers crossed. Don't forget to keep a diary of everything, and email me the details when you're ready.'

Before we terminated the conversation, there was something that didn't make sense to me, and I needed him to clarify it – hadn't he found a CSF leak 'gushing through', when he opened up my head the first time?

There was a slight pause while he considered my question, and then he replied, openly and honestly: Perhaps that hadn't been the case after all. Yes, he had seen CSF clearly flowing out, but it was possible that he had caused it to happen in the process of lifting my temporal lobe, the part of the brain that he couldn't avoid touching during the operation. The site would have sealed up again, on completion of the surgery. Knowing what he knew now, it was more than likely there hadn't been any sort of leak prior to that, or since.

After the telephone call, I didn't experience the elation or relief that perhaps I was expecting to feel. Instead there was an absence of emotion, almost a sense of loss, which I gradually came to understand was the psychological mechanism that kicks in during a period of shock. It was going to take me a while to come to terms with what I'd been told, and adjust to the new reality of my situation. My surgeon wasn't expecting the scopolamine to be the magic solution to my problem, but it could certainly confirm, one way or the other, whether we were now at last on the right track. I trusted Dr Gianoli implicitly, and I was right to do so. Just over two months after he offered his diagnosis, a pair of French doctors published a study, the sole purpose of which was to alert the medical profession to a very unusual and specific phenomenon.

The article, published in the September 2010 edition of *Otology & Neurotology*, drew attention to the possibility of 'unilateral rhinorrhea, with concomitant hyperlacrimation and hypersialorrhea, without a CSF origin, after translabyrithine surgery'. To the man or woman on the street, that amounts to dripping from the nose, and an excessive production of tears and saliva, occurring after an operation involving the balance canals, which may look like a CSF leak but isn't. I was in fact a much more extreme case than the few witnessed by the French doctors, and their patients didn't have SCDS, but Dr Gianoli seemed sure that 'their description just about fits you to a T.' His discovery of the article was truly serendipitous.

Shortly afterwards my surgeon assigned an eponymous label to my very particular set of symptoms. Philippa Syndrome: SCDS with associated rhinorrhea, lacrimation or sialorrhea – where CSF leak has been ruled out – that is most likely secondary to abnormal unilateral parasympathetic stimulation, although this can be a bilateral process. He admitted, however, that it was likely to take him a very long time indeed to figure out exactly what had caused the nerves to react so aggressively.

I had not one, but two, extremely rare head conditions.

18

PHILIPPA SYNDROME

It was bad enough being confronted with the blank looks that the words Superior Semicircular Canal Dehiscence Syndrome generated, but explaining that Parasympathetic Hypersensitive Syndrome was the likely cause of a half a head that filled with unwanted liquid was basically a non-starter. The few times I tried summarising the situation for friends, offering the notion that I simply had a head unlike anyone else's, only tended to re-inforce the feelings of being of extraterrestrial origin.

The European Organisation for Rare Diseases (Eurodis) has put into words the 'painful surrounding psychological desert' that comes hand in hand with very unusual conditions. 'Not only are you affected by a disease about which hardly anything is known, but also nobody understands what you personally endure in your daily life.' First there is the pre-diagnosis maze to contend with, only to be followed by a lack of information and scientific knowledge, and then the social consequences have to be addressed. Living with it has implications in all sorts of aspects, and reduces all the opportunities. According to organ-isations such as Eurodis, there is what they call a psychosocial burden. 'The suffering of the actual condition is aggravated by psychological despair, the lack of therapeutic hope, and an ab-sence of practical support for everyday life.' I had seen this, from the outside looking in, with my son's unique chromosome disorder. There was no medical protocol, and no-one with whom to compare notes. I was now in a very similar position myself, with no set care management pathway.

Resilience could be summed up as not letting life get the better of you, but if only it were as easy as it sounded. I had to force myself to shake off all vestiges of self-pity, and concentrate on the practical task of my patch experiment. It helped to reflect on how lucky I was to have found a professional who did understand, and who was committed to improving my situation. On July 7, I found I had some encouraging news to report to him.

'I had to let you know now that the patch is making a huge difference to the fluid problem. I'll keep recording, and email again early next week. It's a wonderful feeling not to be full of fluid. I can't thank you enough.' I was thrilled; I couldn't wait to share the promising start.

'Hurray. That's great news. I'm so happy for you,' was his swift response.

Four days later, however, it was a very different story.

'I'm afraid things went rapidly downhill after my email. I've managed to last six days on the patches, but the side effects got worse and worse, and I actually had to retreat to my bed today. I'm not planning to put the third patch on in the morning, as I just have to get better.'

'Don't get too discouraged,' Dr Gianoli wrote back. 'We've made a big step forward here. What side effects are you having?'

I wished I hadn't been quite so hasty with my initial response, and it seemed important now that my surgeon should appreciate exactly how poisonous the scopolamine medication could be. As it has the ability to cross the blood-brain barrier, there is always a risk of negative effects on the central nervous system, including sedation, agitation and even delirium.

'I kept a list, which I added to as the days went by,' I told him. 'On day one I very quickly noticed my balance going, and

I felt generally light-headed. The very dry mouth started, which I expected, and I felt pretty drowsy. When I contacted you, I wasn't really concerned about all this as I wrongly assumed things would settle down. Instead it got much, much worse. My mouth just got drier and drier, and then sort of stuck together; the dizziness worsened, and I felt like I had a wobble inside my head; I couldn't use the computer for any length of time, as it made my eyes feel as though they were jumping around; I felt completely drained of energy, and had to struggle to keep my eyes open most of the time – all I wanted to do was lie down, and shut them; my skin became terribly itchy, particularly around my head and face; by about day three, I was getting more and more breathless, and my chest felt very tight – I'm sure my heart was going far too fast; on Sunday I had a red left eye, and my daughter thought my pupils looked dilated, and by that evening I had absolutely no appetite, and had to force myself to eat even tiny amounts of food; however, by Monday, it wasn't just loss of appetite but chronic nausea, which is why I had to go and lie down, as I couldn't do anything properly. Besides all of this, which was bad enough, one of the worst symptoms was the way it affected my mind. After the first couple of days, I felt very, very low indeed, and at the same time, horribly anxious, and on edge. I was totally unable to relax, or rest properly, because of these feelings. The only time I can recall ever feeling anything like that was when I was taking the Diamox last year. All in all, a horrendous experience.'

'By all means take a few days off. You've had just about every side effect that you can get from scopolamine,' my doctor informed me. 'But I think the hard part is over – figuring out what is causing this.'

It was true. The patches had reduced the fluid build-up quite considerably, but from my perspective Devil's Breath was an extremely accurate name for the drug. There was no way I could contemplate taking it on a regular basis – by the end of the trial I had felt more than a little inclined to hurl myself off the nearest tall building. The effects of the drug were disturbing, to put it mildly. On the one hand, I was relieved to know the experiment was confirming the diagnosis of overactive nerves, but on the other hand, I had very good reason to be alarmed about that. There definitely wasn't going to be any easy solution to my complex problem.

I was even more curious now to understand why my symptoms were so much more severe depending on what the weather was doing, and another online hunt revealed a website discussing the whys and wherefores of the autonomic nervous system. It is so-called because it autonomously controls all the involuntary actions of the body, such as breathing and digestion, and is divided into two branches – simplistically, sympathetic being the 'fight or flight system', and parasympathetic 'rest and digest'. The author suggested that it was 'known that the body is shifted more towards the sympathetic dominant state when in high air pressure (ie. sunny days), and shifted to the parasympathetic dominant state during low pressure, rainy days.' If true, and if it was the parasympathetic branch that had gone awry in my case, that would explain why on the low pressure days those particular nerves had so much more opportunity to give me a hard time.

'Understanding the human brain is a great and complex problem,' said neurobiologist Cornelia Bargmann, in an interview for The New York Times in 2015. 'The brain has eighty-six billion nerve cells, and in any mental process millions of them are engaged. Information is sweeping across these millions of neurons.' She is co-chairwoman of the advisory commission for the Brain Initiative, set up to enable the mapping of human brain activity in circuits and networks. 'The brain of the C. elegans worm has already been mapped,' she said. 'Every connection between every nerve cell and the brain – that's roughly 7000 connections, and 300 neurons. Most of what we know about the human nervous system, we have learned from simpler animals.'

Later in the same year as the interview, neuroscientists were shocked by the discovery of two extra neurons in the male worm. They thought they had exhaustively catalogued the nervous system of the species, but it turned out they hadn't paid quite enough attention to the brain in the male. The mystery cells revealed how a supposedly simple brain could be capable of a complex learned behaviour, in this case when to prioritise mating over eating. Perhaps one day, when C.elegans has definitely been fully mapped, the tiny worm, or another small creature, might help unlock the secret of my mysterious head.

Of course I was dealing with a double whammy. In addition to the misbehaving nerves, I had a holey head, and it is very common indeed for SCDS patients to complain of their symptoms being aggravated by low barometric pressure. The precise reason for this is not yet known, but Dr Gianoli was willing to put forward his theory on the subject.

'I suspect the biggest issue is the change in the pressure differential seen at the round and oval windows – one side is the inner ear, reflecting intracranial pressure, and the other side is barometric pressure. When barometric pressure drops, the intracranial pressure is relatively higher than it was prior to the drop. This will bulge the round window outwards, distorting the inner ear membranes. If the pressure differential gets too extreme, there is a rupture.'

As far as finding a way forward in August 2010, there were a couple of matters that could be cleared up relatively quickly. The first was to find out whether a much milder medication called Robinul was up to the job of controlling the aggressive nerve reaction. It wasn't. The other was to rule out any sort of toxic poisoning. I contacted my GP, and provided the name of a suitable expert that would hopefully give an opinion. I had become accustomed to locating all the specialists myself, and this one was at the top of the tree within his profession.

'My GP rang this morning,' I told Dr Gianoli. 'He sounded quite excited, and said it was because he wasn't ever expecting to be contacted by the most eminent toxicologist in Britain. They discussed my case in some detail, and the expert concluded that my problem was almost certainly anatomical. He said it was highly unlikely that any sort of poisoning would have such a specific effect, and that he would expect me to be much more generally ill. He couldn't comment further on exactly what may have happened, but there were no toxicology tests that could be helpfully undertaken. He considers he has ruled out toxic poisoning.'

'That's great news,' he replied. 'I'm glad you could get that sort of consult so easily. It makes me feel better about you having any glands removed, in that we aren't missing something more ominous.'

My surgeon and I had quite quickly moved from discussing causes and medications, to surgical interventions. There are three main pairs of salivary glands. The parotid glands, close to the ears, are the largest; the submandibular, in the shape of a U, reside under the chin bone; the sublingual are under the tongue. In addition, there are multiple minor salivary glands scattered all over the oral cavity. I had established that Professor Lello (doctor no.8), who knew all about these glands, was in the process of retiring, and wouldn't therefore be able to assist me, so the path was leading back to Professor Russell in London (doctor no.11). At my request, Dr Gianoli made email contact with him, to see whether he could throw any light on why salivary glands might behave in such a rogue fashion.

'The vast majority of salivary problems are simply plumbing defects, due to physical obstruction such as a stone or stricture,' the professor explained. 'But there is a very small sub group of patients with highly unusual symptoms, as though there is a defect in the release mechanism.'

Of course it was this sub group that interested us, but further prompting didn't produce any helpful advice.

'I have no explanation,' wrote Professor Russell. 'If you find an answer, I would be very interested to know. You're in uncharted territory – we never resolved our cases.'

It was an ominous start to re-establishing relations with the British medical profession. It would have boosted my confidence no end, if Professor Russell had suggested re-opening my case, or better still undertaking surgery to remove one or more of the glands on the left side of my face, particularly as he was unable to suggest any alternative means of tackling my symptoms. However, it was left to me to specifically request his involvement. We had a rather tense conversation on the telephone, not helped by the fact that I still held the picture of him in my mind as an irascible Rumpelstiltskin from our last encounter. His stance this time seemed particularly bizarre, as he revealed on the phone that he was personally reluctant to remove any glands, not being able to explain the symptoms or the pathological process, and yet he wasn't averse to another surgeon doing this for me. He agreed to send a letter to a Mr Jenkins, with whom I could consult in Edinburgh.

Nearly a year and a half had passed, since I'd jumped off the merry-go-round that a bunch of feckless British doctors had put me on, and I was not relishing the prospect of getting back on it. I certainly wasn't going to leave anything to chance, so I needed to prepare for the worst with this new consultant. I found him online, and studied the profile photograph closely, concluding that he looked reasonably affable. I knew looks could be deceptive though.

I also knew Mr Jenkins (doctor no.12) was a junior version of Professor Russell, and this was confirmed as I watched his tall figure bound energetically up the stone steps into the Georgian building, where months earlier I had spent time discussing my circumstances with Professor Lello (doctor no.8). I had arrived in good time to allow for a suctioning session in a contorted position inside my car, and I bobbed my head up every so often, hoping to catch sight of the man in the picture. I'd always quite fancied the idea of being a private detective on a surveillance operation. It was the chocolate brown suede boots that caught my eye, when he greeted me inside shortly afterwards, as they looked slightly incongruous paired with the dark blue suit and silk tie that completed the outfit. They were obviously a new acquisition – the doctor couldn't seem to take his eyes off them, as he walked towards me in the waiting room. I followed him and the boots up the stairs into a large bright room. He gestured for me to take a seat, and then confirmed that he had received the letter from Professor Russell.

'I've brought this to show you as well,' I said, handing him a short abstract of the article written by the French doctors, the one that made some sense of my nerve abnormality. He barely glanced at it, a clear signal that I might have another battle on my hands. I had rehearsed with Dr Gianoli the key points I would need to cover as simply as possible, and I raced through my summary.

'It seems as though the glands are getting engorged… it causes me great discomfort….medical treatment has been tried….removal of the source of the fluid seems the only sensible option.' Mr Jenkins listened carefully, but I had the distinct impression my words weren't making much of an impact.

'My American surgeon says that, as my case is so unusual, we need to think a little outside the box.'

It was those words that created the spark. Mr Jenkins rose from his chair and, looking me straight in the eye, commenced his lecture.

'I have spent quite a lot of time working in America myself in the past,' he said. 'I think perhaps you need to understand they have a rather different mindset over there. Doctors here do in fact have more experience, and they've seen more patients. We aren't always so ready to rush into things.'

He carried on in the same vein for several more minutes and I could feel my anger bubbling under the surface. I tried not to let it show on my face. I could hardly believe the insensitivity of the man, pontificating about the superiority of British doctors, when those very doctors had forced me to find help overseas.

'You've certainly seen a large number of consultants,' Mr Jenkins commented, having picked up the notes on his desk to refresh his memory. It wasn't said with sympathy, there was a disapproving tone. J for judgmental.

'Well, yes I have,' I replied. 'But it wasn't out of choice, I assure you. I kept being passed from one to another, and still I was getting nowhere.' I wanted to add, 'You're number twelve on my British list', but I didn't think it would be appreciated.

After answering some irrelevant questions about my earlier operations and previous symptoms, which served only to satisfy his curiosity, I steered the discussion back to my salivary glands, and how he could help me now. He had sat back down in the leather desk chair, after examining my face and looking inside my mouth, and seemed keen to show that he had a kinder, more human, side to his nature.

'I am sympathetic to your situation, but I'm just not very convinced that removal of a gland would resolve the symptoms you're getting,' he said. 'I certainly wouldn't remove the parotid gland, with the facial nerve running through it. And of course you would be left with a very prominent scar if the subman-dibular was taken out.' He traced a finger along his neck to emphasise the point.

It was difficult to know how to make headway. We spent the next ten minutes batting arguments backwards and for-wards, and I started to wonder whether he just considered this some sort of sport. My exasperation was now evident.

'If you're reluctant to remove any glands, despite Professor Russell giving his go-ahead and my American surgeon advising it, please could you tell me what you would propose instead. In fact, what would you do if you were me?'

Mr Jenkins was on his feet again. Was another lecture about to begin? He seemed to open his mouth to speak, and then it turned into a smile. There is a surprising variety of smiles that can take shape on a face, and this was the self-satisfied, know-ing kind. Head slightly tipped back, pursed, upturned lips, and a confident look. He shrugged his shoulders.

'I don't know,' he said. 'I admit there's no obvious answer. You're fortunate of course, being an articulate, intelligent per-son. The vast majority of people with rare conditions like yours would never have managed to get any treatment I suspect.'

I wasn't sure whether to congratulate him on his honesty, or round on him for his disturbing complacency. Before we parted company, I made it very clear I was not shifting from my wish for an operation, and so we had to reach a compromise – he wished to discuss the matter with Professor Lello. It wasn't an unquestionable 'no', but it was nowhere near a 'yes' either. When I relayed this state of affairs to my former ally, he chose to distance himself.

'I don't think it would be a good idea to see me,' wrote Professor Lello. 'I don't need convincing. I should really remain on the periphery of any of Mr Jenkins' management plans.'

I'd had enough. They were at it again – sending me round in circles, more concerned about stepping on each others' toes, than trying to resolve the patient's problem. I vented my frustration in an email to Dr Gianoli.

'It's this sort of nonsense that is rapidly driving me insane. One doctor says he wants the other involved, and that one then says he shouldn't get too involved. Meanwhile they don't communicate directly with each other. I have had so many strange things wrong with me that I think they're also terrified to go anywhere near me, and hope I'll either go away, or the problem will miraculously disappear.'

'I'm sorry to hear your frustration, and I certainly understand it,' Dr Gianoli wrote. 'But keep in mind that your situation is unique, and he hasn't yet said no to surgery. Perhaps Mr Jenkins needs to think about it for a bit.'

But four weeks later, if Mr Jenkins was thinking about it he still hadn't conveyed that to me, and he hadn't made any contact with Professor Lello either.

'To be completely frank with you, I'm at breaking point.'

I felt foolish having to admit such weakness to my American surgeon, and almost embarrassed about the behaviour of his counterparts in my country.

'I've been doing battle with the medical system since 2004, and there's only so much a person can take. I'm also hardly getting any sleep, as my son's epilepsy is not under control at the moment. He had five seizures in one night this week. I've had to turn down two dates for his spinal surgery, one in June and one in August, and I can't keep on doing that. I've told the ENT consultants here about that, and still they prevaricate, and do nothing.'

'I spoke with a colleague of mine,' Dr Gianoli replied. 'I'd actually talked to him about your case a while back. He is intrigued, and wants to review your scans and records, and then correspond with you. I'll get him the scans I have, and fill in the details that I know about. He'll then tell me what else he needs.'

The email perfectly illustrated the differences in approach either side of the Atlantic. An American physician, who had never met me, was 'intrigued' and suggesting he review my medical notes, while those who were supposed to be treating me showed little interest or desire to investigate, and bleated 'we've never heard of that happening.' Atul Gawande, the distinguished American surgeon and writer, has stated that for a clinician 'nothing is more threatening to who you think you are, than a patient with a problem you cannot solve', and the result is that 'all too often medicine fails the people it is supposed to help.' I would suggest to him that perhaps some are more easily threatened than others, and the solving of any problem requires a strong desire to do so in the first place. A patient needs most of all to know that the doctor is on their side.

By October my options became clear, as Mr Jenkins sent me a letter. It simply reiterated his position.

'As things stand, I still do not feel that excision of your left submandibular gland will improve your symptoms, but I am happy to discuss this further if you wish to make another appointment.'

He had sought Professor Lello's advice. The advice given to him was 'to consider removing the left submandibular gland, and to undertake a parotid duct tie as well', and yet Mr Jenkins still hadn't shifted his view. Moreover, Professor Russell had been told about the findings in the French doctors' published paper, and yet it hadn't made him any more willing to get involved either.

'It is possible that a selective injury could lead to increased salivary function, but I have never encountered this event,' the professor wrote in an email, via his secretary. 'Thank you for bringing this to my attention.'

Meanwhile, far away in Louisiana, two highly skilled surgeons, Dr McLaughlin and Dr Walvekar – the salivary gland duo, as Dr Gianoli later jokingly referred to them – were bending over backwards to do whatever they could to help me. They read all the information shown to them, they studied my scans, they independently suggested talking to me on the telephone, and then they both conducted thorough question and answer sessions during those long conversations. They listened, really listened, and they explained to me all the options that in their opinion were viable ones. They flatly refused to accept remuneration for all the time and expertise they were giving me. Their rallying response was uplifting, and most of all it offered a way forward. At the end of my talk with Dr McLaughlin, he told me, 'we like unusual things here'. I expressed my astonishment to Dr Gianoli.

'I couldn't imagine, in my wildest dreams, a doctor of any kind saying that to me in this country.'

As the focus was now centred on the activity of my salivary glands, I had requested all the records related to my visit to Professor Russell back in March 2009, a year and a half ago. The Americans understandably wanted to have a look at the specialised scans undertaken. I glanced at the scribbled handwriting on the page of out-patient clinic notes, not expecting to see anything of interest, but I had to do a double take. I took a few minutes to rewind to the events of that spring morning. I clearly recalled sitting with a bowl on my lap, encouraged to let my drool run free, so that they could measure the flow of saliva from inside both my cheeks. The exercise was then repeated, with the added saliva stimulation of a lemon drop in my mouth.

I had been told by the team, quite emphatically, that nothing unusual had shown up during their series of tests, and yet on the piece of paper I was holding, 'minimal flow from the left parotid gland' had been recorded. No one had mentioned it, and yet the whole point of the lengthy investigation that day was to look for any gland abnormalities on the left side of my face. Had this significant little piece of information been disclosed, who knows how much sooner Dr Gianoli could have unravelled the mystery. Right there, in spidery scrawl, was a vital clue that the parotid gland was being abnormally stimulated, and getting engorged.

It was the last straw. If the parotid gland was indeed malfunctioning, the gland Mr Jenkins flatly refused to touch, my escape route to Louisiana would need to be followed yet again. I would have to make my way to Dr Walvekar in Baton Rouge. The assistant professor, a native of Mumbai who had made his home in America, had impeccable credentials of international renown, and fortunately for me salivary glands were his specialised field. He had made it clear on the telephone he wouldn't shirk from taking out two whole glands, if that was the best way of relieving my suffering.

How to finance another trip, and the surgery, was now the greatest concern, and I also needed to consider whether it might be possible to do it alone, to avoid dragging my sister along a third time. Life isn't predictable. It has a habit of throwing up unexpected twists and turns, and it was about to do it to me again.

19

ALRIGHTEE

'Grief comes in waves, paroxysms, sudden apprehensions that weaken the knees and blind the eyes, and obliterate the dailiness of life.' That is how Joan Didion, in her memoir *The Year of Magical Thinking*, described the grief she experienced, after the sudden death of her husband from a heart attack. My father had died shortly before my thirtieth birthday, and the process of grief I encountered then was very similar. I didn't have a chance, however, to prepare myself for going through it again, this time for a beloved animal that departed from our lives without warning.

The death of Maisie in October was totally unexpected, and the extent of the heartbreak equally so. I had never owned a dog before and therefore never lost one, but I did remember my father telling me that he could never have another, after enduring the horrible experience of his dear Laddie, also a spaniel, being put to sleep. Coming from someone who didn't often openly share his feelings, the admission revealed the depth of his sorrow. Maisie had been a part of our family for eight years, leading a healthy and energetic life, until ten days before her final collapse. On thorough examination, the vet had found no obvious reason for her unusual listlessness or reduced mobility, but suspected that the early stages of spondylitis might be the cause, as there was some inflammation along her back – a form of arthritis that often affects the breed. A course of steroids was prescribed, which did the trick, and she perked up considerably. However, a swift and fatal downturn suddenly occurred.

Holding back the tears, I discussed with the vet on the telephone her rapid decline, and he concluded there had most likely been an undiagnosed tumour that had ruptured. I had come close to losing Maisie once before, during the escapade when she fell into the deep hole in the ground, and it seemed a cruel blow to have her taken away so abruptly, just a few months later. To cap it all, Hugh and I were due to attend the funeral of a family friend in Edinburgh the very next morning. We returned home promptly after it, to bury the small, stiff body in a corner of our garden before Amy returned home from school. All three of us were devastated by what had happened.

The next jolt came on New Year's Eve, shortly after eight in the evening to be precise. It was a call from Edinburgh Royal Infirmary – a kidney had become available, and Hugh was required urgently at the hospital for an assessment. A patient on a transplant waiting list in theory has to be organised, and ready to go at short notice, night or day, but in reality, even if the bag is packed, mental preparation is needed too. There was a tense half an hour during which a potential complication with the kidney on offer was carefully considered, and then it was all systems go. I embraced Hugh, and waved him off, as he was driven away into the night.

It was the strangest New Year's Eve I had ever spent, with Patrick asleep in his room, Amy out overnight celebrating with her friends, and not even a dog for company. I felt numb from the shock of the phone call. I sat alone, wondering whether the transplant operation would proceed, and whether I should contact anyone to tell them what was going on. I knew Hugh would be in touch with his mother from the hospital so I sent an email to Georgie, feeling the need to communicate the momentous event that was probably about to take place. No reply came back, but it was New Year's Eve, the night when most people are busy enjoying themselves. Once New Year's Day arrived, my husband was successfully given a new kidney, and the chance to be free from a lifelong dependence on dialysis. It happened on my birthday.

It was an exciting start to 2011, but my stress level now jumped up several notches. In the intervening weeks between Maisie's loss of life and Hugh's new lease of life, a plan had been formulated, and I was expected back in Baton Rouge on January 16. That was only a couple of weeks away, and it was as yet unclear how long Hugh would need to remain in hospital. Complicated arrangements needed to be quickly put in place for his aftercare once he returned home, as well as covering Patrick's support while I was away, since his father would be completely out of action. The schools were on holiday so I had two children to look after, as well as daily trips to and from the hospital in Edinburgh to see the transplant patient, first in the High Dependency Unit and then on a renal ward. I tried to present a calm and cheerful front during these visits, but behind the scenes I was struggling to stay on top of all my responsibilities, and the financial aspects of the forthcoming American expedition were spiralling out of control.

I explained the latest developments to Georgie, who had insisted she must accompany me to America again, as it was going to be another major operation, almost certainly involving the removal of two whole salivary glands. The administrative staff in Dr Walvekar's office had estimated that the operation alone, excluding the requisite tests before it, and our travel and accommodation, may cost around $35,000; the figure could fluctuate by a few thousand dollars or so, they blithely added.

Poor Dr Gianoli was also pulled into the conversation, as I was so flabbergasted by the figures being quoted. I sent him an email, in response to his advice about how it might be possible to compromise on the fees.

'I shall email the hospital manager about their estimate, and make a proposal along the lines you suggest. I used to do a lot of fee negotiating with very expensive photographers and photo studios as a picture editor, so I'll have to put those skills back into practice now. If you're able to find out anything, as you kindly offered, that might help too. I've got to sort this out over the next few days, but at the same time I'm up and down to the hospital (which takes up about three and a half hours), draining my head and caring for my son, so it's going to be a big New Year's challenge for me. By the time I get to Baton Rouge I'll be a nervous wreck, and won't care what they do to me!'

Even with my mother's generous backing once more, the potential costs were impossibly high, and worry about it preoccupied my mind. I also railed inwardly against the injustice of my predicament, unable to come to terms with the fact that I was effectively being expelled from our NHS system yet again. What on earth would happen to someone else in my position, if they weren't fortunate enough to have a parent to bail them out?

Everyone is familiar with stress, but whom better to turn to than Dr Hans Selye, author of the classic text *The Stress of Life*, for an understanding of its mechanisms and effects. 'No one would ever think of checking his conduct as carefully during stress, as he does at a cocktail party. Yet he should. The fact is that a person can be intoxicated with his own stress hormones,' he warns. 'The hormones produced during acute stress are meant to alarm you, and key you up for peak accomplishments. They tend to combat sleep, and insomnia is a powerful stressor in itself.' I was becoming trapped in a vicious circle of worry, overexertion, exhaustion, stress, sleeplessness. As Hans Selye explains, 'the process is comparable to raising the key of a violin, by tightening the strings. There is the tingling sensation, the jitteriness, when we are keyed up too much. This impairs our work, and even prevents us from getting a rest.' The important course of action to counter these effects is to 'find something to put in the place of the worrying thoughts, to chase them away. This is deviation.'

Try as I might, I couldn't find an appropriate form of deviation to take my mind off everything. I was well aware that it was all getting on top of me, and I also recalled that the French doctors had in their case studies identified stress as a factor likely to aggravate the nerve hyperactivity. I attempted to focus on the positive changes for all the family that would be brought about by Hugh's transplant, but a burdensome secret kept getting in the way, one that was under wraps largely for my daughter's benefit. An incident, only weeks earlier, had brought marital matters to a head. During a solemn discussion, my husband and I concluded our relationship had no long-term future. We had had a myriad of strains put on our marriage; they undoubtedly helped derail it, and it was unlikely that even a transplant would put it back on track. Not a word had been said about this to anyone. As all the members of her family were undergoing serious health complications, it seemed imperative to me that the pretence of a stable family life should be maintained for Amy's sake, to prevent any added anxiety or disruption while she completed the important final months of her school education. However, this concealment was starting to take its toll on me.

Happily married or not, my intention was always to give full support if ever a kidney was donated, so I was determined to concentrate on my husband's recovery over the next two weeks, until my mother-in-law took over the caring role while I was away. My sister and I had often joked that my surgeries in the States were my holidays, and I was certainly eagerly anticipating the next one. All I could do was hope that the money issues would somehow fall into place, as I had been assured by Dr Walvekar that he and his colleague were exploring all the avenues they could think of, to try to reduce the sums. One back-up plan was that I should have the operation performed at a small surgery centre by Dr McLaughlin, whereby the costs would be minimal compared to the overheads of the large hospital, in which the Indian surgeon carried out all his work of this kind. Everyone recognised, though, that this would be a less satisfactory outcome, as salivary glands were after all Dr Walvekar's specific field of expertise.

I had every reason to trust these doctors. I was so impressed by their enquiring minds and probing questions, and I believed they illustrated a way of working that Lisa Sanders admired in *Every Patient Tells a Story*. 'Getting a good history is a collaborative process,' she wrote, like 'two writers collaborating on a manuscript, passing drafts of the story back and forth until both are satisfied. What the patient brings to the process is unique: the particular and private facts of his life and illness. And what the physician brings is the knowledge and understanding that will help him order that story, so that it makes sense both to the doctor and the patient.' This way of working was a far cry from the likes of Dr Miller (Doctor No.6) and his rigid, computerised questionnaire.

In effect, I had not one but three physicians bringing their knowledge and understanding – Dr Gianoli, Dr McLaughlin and Dr Walvekar – and I was immensely grateful for that. There was mounting tension, and a significant amount of frustration, as I tried to steer these busy doctors' decisions and work schedules from afar, but a sense of humour helped keep everything on course, particularly in relation to some of the information being shared.

'The "pleasant lady from Scotland" reference made me laugh,' I told Dr Gianoli. 'I presume it's a standard term used in these medical letters, but I've only seen it once in my referral letters over here. I was called "quite a pleasant lady" in a GP's letter, so I seem to have managed to improve a little over the months. I'm wondering what it takes to be described as "an unpleasant lady", or even "quite an unpleasant lady"? Perhaps you can enlighten me.'

'LOL. But you are a pleasant lady! Otherwise I would never have responded to your emails,' Dr Gianoli reassuringly confirmed. 'As for the designation of "unpleasant", I don't think that ever happens. "My mother always said if you can't say something nice about someone, then don't say anything at all" – it most likely relates to that saying.'

I actually found out later, however, that judgmental comments had been far less veiled back in the days when patients didn't have access to their own records. A surgeon has been recorded as having sent a letter to a general practitioner in the 1970s, in which he expressed the view that 'this wretched creature should be prevented from having any more of these ghastly children.'

It felt completely normal to be back in Baton Rouge at the end of January 2011, and I was relieved that Hugh had been discharged just before my departure. The mild weather was a welcome change after several weeks of snow in Scotland. Georgie and I were starting to feel at home in the city, and my chauffeuse was now finding her way around with comparative ease. Our new destination was the Catholic-sponsored Our Lady of the Lake, one of the largest private medical centres in Louisiana. The arrangement of a group of huge, brownish pink buildings looked like gigantic Lego blocks set down at the side of the tree-lined street. The medical centre had been established in 1923, but the Franciscan Missionaries of Our Lady date back to 1854, when seven groups of Franciscan Sisters banded together in France. They expanded from there across Europe, and into Asia and America.

We received an extremely warm welcome once we'd ascended to the Head and Neck Center, greeted with hugs by Nancy, the smartly dressed Practice Manager. 'How y'all doin?' she enquired enthusiastically, and 'poor baby' she exclaimed, when my sister requested the use of Nancy's back room, to enable me to lie down and pump out the saliva build up from my head. 'Alrightee', she chirped, in agreement to any of our suggestions. The two surgeons from her team of seven specialists proved equally charming – Kevin McLaughlin the slightly smaller, mischievous one of the pair, and Rohan Walvekar, the tall, dark gentleman with an engaging smile and impeccable manners.

First thing that morning I had been in a scanner again for half an hour, and Dr Walvekar explained to me that the MR sialography, to evaluate my salivary ducts, was carried out with very new technical equipment. The combination of strange, avant-garde background music, with loud bangs at unexpected moments, and a long section in which a swarm of bees seemed to have invaded my head, with their buzzing steadily increasing in volume, hadn't been a relaxing start to the day after our late arrival the night before. The radiographer wasn't immediately able to locate anything out of the ordinary on the scans but, when Dr Walvekar studied them very closely with him, clear evidence of an abnormality on the left side emerged. The duct of the parotid gland was definitely dilated, whereas the right one looked normal. Of course the technology employed in London in 2008 had also supposedly been bang up to date, but had nevertheless failed to pinpoint an irregularity. It was highly improbable the difference in the salivary duct hadn't existed at that time, so either the equipment hadn't been up to the job, or the scan reviewers had not been thorough enough.

The surgeons now had reliable evidence that removal of both the parotid and submandibular salivary glands would be the most hopeful permanent solution to my problem, but there was still the money question to resolve, and everyone seemed to be skirting around it. Georgie and I sat waiting again outside Nancy's office, intending to discuss the thorny issue with her, and hoping for another 'alrightee' response. We were sure it wouldn't be as straightforward as that, and were both finding it difficult to relax with such uncertainty hanging over us. One of the pleasurable aspects of the American expeditions was getting to know my sister much better, and I was noticing changes in her behaviour over the last couple of years. Her assertiveness had increased, and she was far less reticent to express her wishes. On the plane she had insisted to the cabin staff that we needed to change seats, selecting empty ones that would give better opportunity for my bizarre head practices, and she was now starting to get impatient about the delay in talking to our new friend.

At last Nancy appeared, and after a short discussion with us in her room and then a brief telephone conversation which left us none the wiser, she directed us down to the finance department where I needed to fill in paperwork related to my hospital admission. The broad-shouldered woman at the information desk took a few details.

'That's a thick, thick head of hair,' she said, as I began to turn around, looking for a seat. 'That's real pretty.'

I was just absorbing the compliment, smiling and wishing my hair was shiny and sleek rather than double thick, when she shifted her attention to Georgie.

'Not everyone can wear that colour,' she remarked, perusing my sister's shorter, naturally grey locks.

Georgie's face fell. Her hair was a regular source of annoyance to her, and she could have done without the cryptic comment. We always had to make a mental adjustment to allow for the cultural differences during our stays, as there was no doubt that Americans were more outspoken than we were used to. We usually loved them for it, and it certainly amused us. Nancy had accounted for her lateness by informing us that her fourteen-year-old daughter's menstrual cycle had just started for the first time, and she had had to leave the office to take her home from school. That was already slightly too much information, but then she added that her daughter was late starting and, for reasons she didn't clarify (thankfully), Nancy was glad about that. Sitting in the clinic waiting area during the morning, we had both listened in amazement to patients exchanging stories about their ailments without holding back, and sometimes even about the physicians that attended to them. It simply wouldn't happen in Britain.

A young black woman came to collect us from where we sat in view of the hair inspector, and led us through an underground warren of aisles and cubicles to a small partitioned space. I sat down diagonally opposite to her at the table, and she began asking questions about my personal circumstances, writing the answers neatly on a large form. I frequently had to spell out unfamiliar names for her. Once the process was complete, she swivelled the form round to my side of the table, and pointed to a huge blank space.

'Could you please fill in that section for me,' she said, putting her pen down in front of me. 'I need you to write there all the outgoings you have in your family each month, and all the income earned by yourself and your husband. Can you itemise everything, and keep the figures as accurate as you can be in the circumstances. Please also explain why you have travelled here from your home country. I'll leave you to get on with it, and I'll come back shortly.'

I looked at my sister in dismay. No-one had clearly explained what might by achieved by this exercise, and my head was throbbing painfully. I just wanted to go back to our hotel and lie down – it had been a long day. We had to hope that some sort of grant might be applied to reduce the medical fees to within an affordable range, so I grabbed the pen and started scribbling furiously. The words came pouring out in a jumble: the surgeries, the rare conditions, the disabled son, the kidney transplant, and the enormous cost of it all, emotionally and financially. Then I had to grapple with the figures, trying to remember approximate amounts for all our monthly bills and every other item of family expenditure, not to mention the cost of the previous two American medical trips. I checked with my sister that I hadn't overlooked anything. The more I wrote the more tired and frustrated I became. Apart from sending me into a depression, I wasn't sure I could see the point of transcribing the miserable list, and why did the hospital need so much detailed, private information?

I handed the sheet of paper to the clerk on her return. Georgie and I then made our way back to the hotel rooms. It was late on Monday, and we were both worn out. I was supposed to have an operation either with Dr Walvekar in two days' time at Our Lady of the Lake, or with Dr McLaughlin the day after next in a surgery centre we hadn't even set eyes upon (in that order of preference), and yet we still didn't know which would happen. Nancy had promised to call the next day, that's all we had to go on. The suspense was exhausting us, and my sister's wish, to have a clear plan of action laid out by now, had not come to fruition.

On Tuesday morning, Georgie drove me to the Ear and Balance Institute, and I was able to talk through with Dr Gianoli the events of the previous day, including the findings from the sialogram. I left having been reassured by him that everything would sort itself out over the next twenty-four hours, and he asked me to stay in touch and visit again after the surgery, before we flew home. The call came through from Nancy during the afternoon. We had eaten a sandwich lunch prepared in our little kitchenette, and decided we couldn't risk leaving the rooms until we'd heard from her, as we weren't confident that the number we'd provided for Georgie's mobile phone was accurate; the correct code for its use in Louisiana was proving elusive. The call was well worth staying in for – to my utter astonishment, Nancy told me that the nuns had decided that the operation, and the stay in their hospital, would be provided free of charge, and that Dr Walvekar should be my surgeon. I asked her to repeat what she'd just told me to be sure there was no misunderstanding, as I was struggling to take in the scope of the generosity being extended to us. Georgie scrutinized my face as I smiled and nodded during the conversation.

'I can't quite believe this,' I said, replacing the receiver. 'All that writing I did when we were down in the finance section yesterday, it was for the Franciscans nuns. They've read my story, and they don't want us to pay anything, Georgie. Nancy said we don't need to worry about the money any more.'

We were both dumbfounded, and I felt guilty about my earlier annoyance. If only they had explained the process that was underway, I would gladly have written them a book.

Early on Thursday morning, before the operation, I was wheeled round to have a CT scan of my head and neck. I calculated it was my ninth. The smiley radiographer was a very friendly man, and once I explained what I was in for, he took delight in telling me the story of his father who had had a salivary gland stone when the radiographer was a child.

'It would swell up very suddenly, and to enormous proportions, at mealtimes,' he told me with glee. 'I used to ask my friends to come round to have a look. "I bet your dad can't do that!" I'd say to them.'

The surgery was the longest one yet, lasting five hours. Dr McLaughlin, who was performing his own operations in the same hospital that day, told me later he had come round to see me but I was still 'three sheets to the wind', and Dr Gianoli telephoned Georgie to find out how I was. They were both surprised by the length of time I'd been unconscious, and I was touched when I heard about their concern. Dr Walvekar had performed an excellent, thorough operation, completely removing two whole glands, and it had left me with a long but neat wound running down the crease at the front of my ear, and then in a slanting line parallel to my jaw. My battle scars were multiplying at an impressive rate. The small tube draining fluid away ('your little friend', as Dr McLaughlin called it), to help the healing process and reduce the chance of infection, had to stay in place until I returned to the clinic a week later, and I now had a very crooked smile. Smiling, eating and talking were all painful in any event, as my face and jaw were so swollen and bruised.

It was sad to say all our farewells when the time came. I didn't know whether I would see my wonderful doctors again. I distributed thank you notes and gifts, and did my best to convey to them how much I appreciated their kindness. Whatever happened in terms of the nerve symptoms, I knew they had gone out of their way to come to my aid, and I would never forget that. A few important words needed to be shared with Nancy too. Georgie and I had agreed during the recovery week that I should propose that I pay her the specific sum of money that related just to Dr Walvekar's surgery fee. We had never imagined that the Franciscan Sisters would offer to treat me free of charge, and I didn't want to take advantage of their generosity beyond what was absolutely necessary. Someone else could benefit from the relatively small amount that I was contributing, and it still left an enormous subsidy. I reached an understanding with Nancy, and we shook hands on it.

'Alrightee,' she said.

20

THINGS WERE GOING BACKWARDS

Eating a tea scone was never going to be the same enjoyable experience again. A true British scone is different to an American one. As cook Andrea Geary has explained, 'It's all about the batter, the butter, and even the pronunciation of the word scone.' Because there is minimal fat content in the British version, the consistency is drier, and the loss of two large salivary glands turned its consumption into an anxiety-inducing embarrassment. On more than one mortifying occasion a layer of dough wedged itself across the whole roof of my mouth, making speech an impossible feat and it was unlikely the world of fashion and beauty would ever catch up with my trend-setting style of teeth caked in white gunge. The only answer was to steer clear of cloying substances from now on.

Salivary glands are there for a reason. The saliva they produce keeps the mouth moist. It helps protect teeth and gums from decay, and aids food digestion. There was now no doubt that my left-sided glands had been playing up, but there were nevertheless many downsides from having two of them taken away. A dry mouth became a permanent bother, especially during the night when it woke me regularly; deep cracks at the corners of my lips started to appear like those a cook dreads, when removing a cake from the oven (to continue the baking theme);

and frequent visits to a dental hygienist were now necessary, to ensure no damaging effects were overlooked inside my mouth. These were long-term issues, but the short-term priority was to restore a relatively normal appearance, and establish what had happened to the fluid build-up. I repeatedly puckered my lips and puffed out my cheeks, assiduously following Dr Walvekar's mouth exercises to combat the nerve palsy, and I emailed photographs of my gradually healing face for him to peruse. By the end of February the scar was looking considerably less angry, but my mouth still remained stubbornly lop-sided.

'Give it a few more weeks for the wounds to settle down,' my surgeon wrote. 'The firmness around the jaw is expected. Let's keep in touch weekly to monitor your progress.'

The most remarkable change to my face had happened overnight, immediately after the operation. The very dark vein running across the lower half of my cheek, which I had mentioned to Dr Gianoli when a CSF leak was still suspected, had vanished in an instant. It was one of a number of diagnostic clues that a series of British doctors had chosen to ignore, and its sudden disappearance confirmed that it had been connected to the over-stimulation problem.

'Like you say, it was probably engorged,' Dr Gianoli agreed, when I told him it had gone. 'When you had the surgery, I expect it was ligated, as well as the vessels feeding into it. I suspect the vein was engorged because the gland was.'

One of the worst offenders when it came to a lackadaisical approach to my case had been Mr Scott (doctor no.10), rather more focused on his honeymoon, I guessed, than his patient. In June 2009, before leaving on the first trip to Louisiana, I had written to the private hospital where the consultation with him had taken place, and was astonished when a staggeringly large bouquet arrived in response to my letter. Four sizable vases were needed to give homes to all the gorgeous blooms. The gift was probably supposed to have a silencing effect, but my inbuilt aversion to being fobbed off leapt into action – as far as I was concerned, the flowers were an admission of guilt.

I requested a full investigation into Mr Scott's dismissive comments during our discussion, the haphazard process he had overseen for testing the fluid I provided, and the long delay before his couple of written sentences informed me that he wanted nothing more to do with my problem.

I had quite enough on my plate without stirring up trouble within the medical profession, but when the Head of Clinical Services got involved, and informed me that Mr Scott conducted his practice at the hospital 'as an independent contractor', basically washing his hands of the matter and suggesting the consultant address any issues with me directly, I decided to take it to the next level.

The statutory purpose of the General Medical Council is supposedly to regulate doctors, and ensure good medical practice, so it seemed to be my obvious next port of call. I was encouraged when an administrator readily agreed to look into the matter, but concern set in when it was suggested during a telephone conversation that there was 'a grey area' when it came to consultants in private practice, as opposed to the NHS. Their investigation proceeded within a 'Fitness to Practise' directorate, which already rang alarms bells for me. I wasn't trying to lose the man his job, rather to ensure there was some regulation over how doctors in such senior positions behaved. Their enquiry centred on checking that Mr Scott was who said he was, and establishing that no other complaints had been made against him at his various workplaces. Once complete, a black mark was placed against his record because of my unsatisfactory encounter, but nothing whatsoever was done to prevent it happening again.

That led me to involve the Care Commission, shortly before the end of 2009. It took many months of emails and letters, an initial half-hearted investigation, followed by a thorough and detailed re-investigation at my insistence, and then at long last justice. Shortly before I departed for the salivary gland removal operation, a letter had arrived which upheld every single one of my complaints against the private hospital, and about the way my treatment had been mismanaged by Mr Scott. Moreover, a number of changes were being implemented to prevent a reoccurrence – if at first you don't succeed, try, try, try again.

The enquiry into Mr Scott was quite separate from the clinical negligence claim being handled by my lawyer, which related to the first SCDS surgery in Manchester, and was the means of seeking financial compensation. There are always two aspects to such a claim: liability, showing a breach of duty of care alongside evidence that the doctor acted in a manner no other similar professional would have done, as well as causation, which means that the breach did indeed cause damage. In the eyes of the law, the defendant can only be liable for damage if it was the foreseeable consequence of the breach of duty.

Such cases tended to take a long time to reach conclusion, but they couldn't drag on indefinitely, as a claim had to be filed within three years of knowledge of the harm caused – known as limitation in the legal world. The first stage involved finding a suitable expert witness, another surgeon with the relevant expertise to review all the details of my case, and determine whether he would have acted differently. This process had got off to an inauspicious start, as the first candidate failed to show a grasp of the issues in hand, and then revealed a latent bias against Americans when he let slip a remark that doctors in the States were only capable of reading medical studies if they were written in English. It presented a good opportunity for some humorous chiding of Dr Gianoli, for his hopeless inadequacy at not being able to read the article referred to, in Dutch. The second potential expert looked much more promising, and I visited him in London for an interview and examination, before he began his careful trawl through the mountain of paperwork and scans.

The transplant patient was meanwhile recovering well, and early in March another medical turnaround knocked me off my feet. I shared the uplifting news about my son's spine with Dr Gianoli.

'Patrick has scoliosis which is now at eighty degrees,' I explained, referring to the curvature which everyone had thought would make surgical correction a necessity, to maintain a pain-free quality of life for my son. 'The incredible discovery happened on Friday, as the specialist could see that his back is not going to get a lot worse. The x-ray showed the growth is nearly complete. The surgeon was also surprised to see that his pelvic area was stable which meant, if he did operate, it wouldn't be as far down the spine as he'd anticipated.'

There had been a gap of fifteen months since Patrick's last x-ray, and surgery had been put on hold while my own operations continued apace, but it was turning out to be a delay with a bright and shiny silver lining. During those months the spine had not deteriorated to the extent anticipated, and the surgeon suggested my husband and I take the weekend to decide whether or not we still wanted him to operate. The risks for such a major intervention were very high indeed because of Patrick's epilepsy not being under control, and his severe learning disabilities making for a dangerously complicated recovery period. Added to this, the potential benefits were now considerably reduced. Spinal fusion with instrumentation leaves the patient with a rigid backbone, literally poker stiff. It took us much less than a weekend to decide against an operation, and when the spinal surgeon discharged Patrick altogether, months later, he agreed it had proved to be absolutely the correct decision.

Things were looking up for two family members, but they weren't quite as rosy when it came to my head case. By March, it was very apparent that although the excess fluid had definitely subsided, the problem remained a substantial one. By doing an exercise similar to the one Dr Gianoli had asked me to do the previous year, recording the times of day I removed the liquid and how long it took just to keep it at a manageable level, I estimated that instead of spending a minimum of two and a half hours a day, Dr Walvekar had managed to reduce it to about one and a quarter. Definitely progress. Applying an evil scopolamine patch brought with it the same debilitating side effects (in fact even worse than before), but it did dry everything up noticeably.

'Well, I think that tells us that you are still getting abnormal parasympathetic stimulation,' concluded Dr Gianoli. 'There is reduced baseline fluid, because you don't have the two major salivary glands, but you still have minor salivary glands, as well as nasal secretions. The scop patch reduces the secretions. We've got you half the way there so far.'

Interestingly, Dr Gianoli mentioned that he had recently met a new SCDS patient who had experienced a hypersalivation problem. I started to get a little excited that I might no longer be a solitary sufferer of what we liked to call Philippa Syndrome, until I learned that the patient's reaction had settled of its own accord, relatively quickly too, in the weeks following her surgery. In her case, the indications were that surgical trauma or inflammation had been the trigger.

'There are lots of variations on how any one disease affects any one patient,' he told me. 'We are all much more different physiologically than we had thought in the past. There is also a lot we still don't know about the human body.'

There was certainly quite a lot that no-one seemed to know about my body. Apart from what to do about my weird, un-stoppable fountain, there was another matter increasingly occupying my mind – the hole on the right side of my head, the one that hadn't been repaired, and had lain undetected for years. I had quite a few reasons to believe it was starting to make its presence felt in troublesome ways.

'Something a little disturbing happened on Sunday morning,' I told Dr Gianoli. 'I was standing at the check-out in a tiny supermarket, and I had a sudden and fairly extreme vertigo experience. If I hadn't been up by the counter, leaning against it, I wouldn't have been able to keep my balance as it was severe. The episode passed quite quickly, and I've tried not to dwell on it. It would be seriously depressing if all that was to start up again.'

Over the course of the next few months I agreed to experiment with drugs again. The diuretic Dyazide proved to be just as intolerable as it had the first time, a spray called Atrovent made no impact on anything at all, and Amitriptyline, most commonly used as an antidepressant, made me feel slightly inebriated and not quite with it most of the time. It wasn't an entirely unpleasant sensation, but as I wasn't depressed and it was a hindrance not being able to locate my parked car each time I tried to return to it in a daze, there seemed little point in continuing with the medication after a trial of six weeks, and no fluid reduction.

I hadn't let up on my own research efforts, and decided it was worth a try to calm the nerves by means of supplements. The body produces GABA (gamma-amino-butyric acid), the primary function of which is to prevent over-stimulation. Taurine and GABA are in fact two of the major inhibitory, or relaxing, neurotransmitters of the brain. When GABA levels drop, the body loses control over the brain nerve cells, and then the neurons become electrically hypersensitive. GABA is not well absorbed if taken on its own, as it does not easily cross over into the brain, but scientists had discovered not long ago that the same receptors are used by these two brain chemicals. GABA levels in the brain are raised by Taurine, and the best way to increase GABA is to take the two in tandem, thus supposedly making the nerves remain calm. To achieve this ideal, I stocked up with B6 and N-acetyl cysteine tablets, and gobbled them up daily. I didn't notice any improvement, but it was impossible to know whether that was because of inadequate dosages. Worse than that, another recording of the fluid suctioning exercise in July indicated that the average time had crept back up from about one and a quarter hour, to nearly two. Things were going backwards.

By the middle of the year, Dr McLaughlin had become involved again, and it was he who suggested the trial of Amitripytline. I had another long chat with him on the telephone, and the new plan we discussed was an operation which would involve both him and Dr Gianoli – cutting, or sectioning, the nerves. Dr McLaughlin would lop the ones running up through my nasal passages, and Dr Gianoli those passing through the middle ear. We all seemed to agree it was the next step, but not a guaranteed solution.

'I have not forgotten that one of the disadvantages of this approach was the possibility of the nerves regenerating after a while,' I wrote to Dr Gianoli. 'But I was encouraged by your conversation with Dr Black about that, and perhaps you've already discussed that aspect with Dr McLaughlin?'

'Well, the nerves may not be a sure thing – just like the parotid and submandibular glands were not a sure thing,' was his guarded response.

December 2 was the date lined up for the fourth return to Louisiana, and this time my operation would be in the small surgery centre, keeping the costs to a minimum. It was agreed that I would need three tests before the operation, to evaluate my right ear and the potential SCDS symptoms. Dr Gianoli was taking my concerns seriously.

Pierre Sollier, in *Listening for Wellness*, explains the role of the eyes in what he calls the vestibule-vision link. 'Our eyes, we are likely to think, exist only for vision, to thread a needle, watch a movie or voraciously read a mystery. The fact is, though, that about twenty percent of the eye's capacity is involved in simply maintaining our balance. When balance is poor, that percentage is even higher. In that case, the processing of visual information slows down, since the eyes are even more engaged in maintaining balance. In the extreme, it may even become difficult to maintain eye contact.'

'I've started to get the feeling I used to have often when driving,' I told Dr Gianoli. 'I really want to close my eyes, and I have to force them to stay open. Driving at night is an absolutely horrible experience, and I can't do it for any distance. My balance seems to be getting worse all the time. I was with my daughter a few weeks ago in her school hall, full of people milling around as it was a careers convention. It was dreadful – I had to steer myself carefully around the room, trying to avoid holding onto her which I was desperate to do. A teenage girl definitely doesn't want to be seen by her peers, with an unstable, weird-looking mother clinging onto her arm. If I turned my head too quickly to look at something, I would almost topple over. I found it an incredibly difficult half an hour, and couldn't wait to get out of the hall.'

Some of my SCDS symptoms were hard to distinguish from those brought on by the nerve complication, but I had nevertheless been rapidly reaching a miserable conclusion.

'In the low pressure, changeable weather that we get a lot in Scotland, I have a nasty pain around the back of my head, and some very unpleasant, stabbing pains too,' I bemoaned. 'My whole head feels as though it is in some kind of clamp. I can't believe anyone should feel the way I feel, and I'm starting to conclude it will only change if my right side is repaired.'

P.J. Haybach, a registered nurse, and author of *Inner Ear Balance and Dizziness Disorders*, suggests that 'to really "get it", an inner ear balance disorder has got to be lived and felt, minute-to-minute, hour-to-hour, day-to-day, for weeks to years on end. Simply reading about it loses a little something in the translation.'

I really got it, that's for sure. I'd lived it now for years on end, and I was slowly trying to build up the courage to see if I could put a stop to it once and for all.

21

DECISION TIME

A group of scientists at University Campus Suffolk tested the accuracy of twenty well-known sayings related to speed. 'At the speed of light' was the fastest, covering 300000000 metres per second. 'Before you know it', suggesting how fast electrical impulses travel along nerves in our bodies, came a relatively slow eighth, at one hundred metres per second, just ahead of 'a bat out of hell'. It's hard to comprehend how they achieved such precise measurements, but nevertheless their findings weren't going to help answer the question of whether electrical impulses could be stopped in their tracks, thereby markedly improving the quality of my life.

I had returned home after the coordinated effort to attempt this by Dr Gianoli and Dr McLaughlin, the former exploring my middle ear and the latter undertaking what proved to be a very uncomfortable approach through my sinus, to try to remove the unwanted innervation to the eye, nose and oral areas. Intense pain, across my forehead and behind my eyes, lingered for weeks. I was under strict instruction to carry out regular sinus rinses to prevent any infection taking hold, and I needed to keep my left eye moistened with drops. In the first month there appeared to be what Dr Gianoli described as 'a sputtering neural stimulation that is dying out', but on Friday January 13,

2012, six weeks on from the surgery, I felt it was time to face up to reality.

'It seems an appropriate day to tell you that I'm afraid I'm back to square one,' I wrote to tell him. 'Once I was off the antibiotics everything seemed to get very bad. The pain was terrible (probably just post-surgery stuff), and the fluid seemed to be back to its old pattern. That's how it still is now. I really don't think there has been any improvement I'm afraid – goodness knows, I wish I could say the opposite. To look on the bright side, the pulsatile tinnitus in my left ear seems to have gone for good. Do you think it was being caused by that little remnant of loose bone you found and removed?'

'You had a small bit of conductive gap in the left ear that probably enhanced the sound of the pulsations,' he explained. 'Now that the little piece of bone is gone, you don't have the conductive gap, and hence you don't hear the pulsations.'

It wasn't that the nerve operation hadn't had any effect. It had. Now only my right eye could shed tears – something I discovered to my consternation one day when I found myself, while out driving in the car, suddenly blinded by tears. Half blinded as it turned out, as the left eye remained stubbornly dry. Watery drips no longer fell from my nose, which they had regularly done during all the dog walks. I discovered gels, pastilles, sprays and mouthwashes that I never knew existed to counteract a dry mouth, and a bottle of water became my regular travelling companion. I was definitely a drier version of my former self. But somehow or other, excess fluid was still being generated inside my face, still getting engorged and still causing pressure and pain as it built up. Those damned nerves had no intention of giving up without a fight.

It wasn't until July, when I chose to spend some spare time reading about studies on rats, that I realised the nerves perhaps hadn't had to put up such a fight after all. I discovered that the sectioning of nerves (chorda tympani) running through the middle ear of the long, thin-tailed creatures had *not* caused any changes in saliva secretion. 'The mechanisms underlying the effects of denervation are still not understood,' concluded the academic paper.

With each passing month I was coming closer to acceptance that I was never going to return to full health. I must be an eternal optimist as I hadn't yet given up hope of that, but the chances of finding a solution to the nerve problem were slipping away, and in the meantime body parts were disappearing – first two large glands, and now nerve endings. A course of acupuncture, with twenty-seven needles at a time (I counted them for Dr Gianoli to satisfy his curiosity), hadn't helped either. My involvement with an online support forum, for SCDS sufferers around the world, proved to be a stepping stone towards a deeper understanding of the lifelong effects of the condition.

Dr Gianoli had first made me aware of the forum at the time of my revision surgery in the summer of 2009, but I had rather arrogantly informed him that having coped so long without it, I wasn't sure joining would particularly help me at that point. By the end of 2011, however, I could see the wider picture. It wasn't just a question of finding support for me, it was a matter of providing it for others, and I had amassed a considerable amount of useful information that I could pass on. And so it was that I came into contact with a wide mix of people, the vast majority of whom had experienced similar difficulties in obtaining their diagnosis, and a large number had also been through surgical procedures with very varying outcomes. There were countless cases of substandard care, overlooked symptoms, and bureaucratic bungling. It brought home to me what a complex condition we were all struggling to cope with, and how much there was still to learn about it.

As with most online activity, there were pros and cons to the forum. The biggest plus point was the opportunity to communicate for the first time with many kind people who completely understood all the problems having SCDS entailed, and to hear their stories. There were numerous pieces of practical advice that could be exchanged, but opinions of members could never be relied upon as a source of accurate medical information.

Just as happens in the offline world, certain personalities occasionally dominated proceedings in a negative way, and angry interchanges erupted. For several years I did my best to help those who seemed most in need, some of them at their wit's end. It was probably an important turning point for me, to redirect some of my obsessive searching for health solutions for myself into guidance for others. I found I could empathise intuitively. I didn't need to try to put myself in their shoes – nine times out of ten I'd already been in them.

The tests on my right, un-operated ear in December 2011 had shown further deterioration compared to Dr Gianoli's earlier test results, and I had a feeling that time wasn't on my side. I already had some permanent hearing loss which my doctor strongly suspected was a result of the hole, and I didn't want to lose any more. Neither did I want my symptoms, which were returning slowly but surely (as well as differently to how they had been the first time), to speed up and incapacitate me. Dr Lloyd Minor's words, when asked in an interview about the first batch of identified SCDS patients, were never far from my mind: 'The decision point for surgery is based on whether the person can control the problem, or the problem controls them.'

Dr Gianoli and I had a number of conversations about bilateral SCDS. He explained that there was no straightforward answer as to whether a repair on one side would be sufficient or not.

'There is great variety in individuals, and that variety can be the consequence of many things,' he said. 'How long the patient has been experiencing symptoms, how much the inner ear has stretched to compensate, and also whether further damage has occurred causing a fistula or other inner ear complications. Repairing one side will often put right the autophony issues, but the balance and dizziness may not be resolved.'

I knew from another of his patients on the forum that an analogy of a mother and two children was appropriate, the brain being the mother and the ears her children. Following the old adage that a mother is only as happy as her saddest child, the brain is only as happy as the saddest ear. Moreover, the ears work together, and above all they need stability. A bilateral patient may have had one operated ear made stable, but the other ear would then be trying to better its relationship with that ear, which has become the stronger of the two, and so the struggle would continue. The brain is meanwhile busy trying to compensate for every change that is occurring, and the compensation can't stop until everything is stable.

To enable me to make a firm decision about proceeding with a surgical repair on my second ear, I had to understand more about what made people like me symptomatic in the first place. After all, the available scientific evidence suggested that the bony defect is a developmental or congenital process, and yet patients tended not to exhibit symptoms until a second event.

'Very few children exhibit symptoms, even though the rate of finding SCDS on a CT scan is the same for adults and children,' confirmed Dr Gianoli. 'We do know for sure that some people have holes (not just thin bone), and yet no symptoms. My suspicion is that all SCDS patients are asymptomatic until a second event, such as trauma (direct or, as in your case, barotrauma from air flight) or pressure altering occurrences.'

'But for years and years I have had less severe symptoms from my right side where there's a hole, and I still can't pinpoint what traumatic event might have caused the hole. Is anything else involved – just general wear and tear, and getting older?' I questioned.

'In general, I believe it's a pressure phenomenon,' was his measured response. 'The older we get, the more lax the round and oval windows inside the ear become, from the repeated pressure strains. I suspect that the windows get stretched to a critical point where there is increased compliance in the inner ear, and then the entire inner ear "jiggles" with pressure. Not everyone recognises the second event. It could just be the straw that breaks the camel's back – something that seems innocuous, but creates the last bit of pressure to cause the breakdown. In your case, the flight was the last straw for the left side. As for your right side, I don't know, but there are a number of patients for whom it isn't obvious what caused the onset of symptoms.'

This discussion got me thinking some more, and produced another round of questions for my ever-patient surgeon. I recognised that I'd had imbalance and associated anxiety for many years before I became pregnant in my mid thirties, but it was at that point that the imbalance became more pronounced, I was often incredibly tired, and I developed a permanent fear of certain environments, especially large shops. Never having been pregnant before, I had no way of knowing whether this was something mothers-to-be often encountered. In the later weeks of the pregnancy I learned that I had developed pre-eclampsia, a dangerous condition involving very high blood pressure, which can result in the death of the foetus and the mother too. I related the story to Dr Gianoli.

'I assumed at the time that my increasing dizziness and general instability were related to the pre-eclampsia. My daughter had to be induced five and a half weeks early because my blood pressure had rocketed, and it was a very long and complicated ventouse delivery. Things, however, got worse. I came perilously close to dying because a blood clot developed, and I was only saved by the swift reaction of a surgeon who threw himself on top of my stomach to clear the clot. A blood transfusion followed. However, the more interesting part of the story is that the doctors couldn't work out why my blood pressure wouldn't go back to normal once my baby had been delivered – as you know, that's normally what happens with pre-eclampsia. In my case it quickly shot up again, and they really struggled to get it under control. I was kept in hospital for ten days, and then allowed to leave with medication for the blood pressure. After about a month or so, everything settled back to normal. A tricky question, I know – is any of that likely to be related to SCDS? The doctors said they had never seen anything like it before, and the London hospital was one very used to dealing with pre-eclampsia.'

'Well, I have seen it before, and I think it *is* related,' said Dr Gianoli. 'From an experiential standpoint, I think pregnancy is the cause for the onset of symptoms in a lot of patients with SCDS, especially if they have a difficult vaginal delivery, or if they have pre-eclampsia.'

I had had both. Superior Semicircular Canal Dehiscence Syndrome had probably been affecting me in even more ways than I'd realised.

My un-operated side appeared from the later, accurate CT scans to have a hole about the same size as the one that had been repaired. If I was ever going to get it fixed, I knew I would only trust Dr Gianoli to do it. The unexplained problem with the nerves was the main stumbling block – how could I be sure I wouldn't end up with the same torment on the second side, and then be stuck for the rest of my life having to pump fluid out of not one, but two areas of my head? It was a prospect that kept me awake at night, wondering whether or not to take a gamble. I had a much better covering of bone over the nerve centre (the geniculate ganglion) on my right side, but as we still didn't know whether that was relevant or not, I couldn't rely on it making the saving difference. I told another SCDS sufferer in England how I felt.

'I've been asking Dr Gianoli loads of questions about my next surgery, and the more questions I ask, the more anxious I get. I just dread coming out worse than I go in. How am I ever going to resolve that problem? I know the operation's got to happen.'

Amy was approaching the end of her schooling in the summer, and then she would be told about her parents' decision to separate. I had confronted one significant issue in my life, and now I had to be decisive and courageous about another. I focused my mind on the changes I wanted to make for my future as a divorced mother of two children, one of whom had multiple disabilities. I knew it wasn't going to be easy, but it might be considerably less stressful without that hole in my life.

In May, I indicated to Dr Gianoli that I was ready to agree to the new surgical approach that he was now using for many of his SCDS repairs – a combination of drilling through the mastoid behind the ear, and a mini craniotomy with a small incision through the skull. This different method meant less risk all round compared to a craniotomy, less pain, and much less chance of damaging the brain's temporal lobe. The size of the hole in my balance canal, and its location, also made this approach an appropriate one for me – the surgeon always had to make that judgment case by case.

Dizziness is insecurity itself, and insecurity was not something that was going to be in short supply in the next phase of my life. I decided I had better set about eliminating the dizziness, and to do that I first had to eliminate the hole.

22

MEASURE TWICE, CUT ONCE

I had learned a new Southern expression in the spring, when Dr Gianoli told me he was in hog heaven. The Ear and Balance Institute had moved out of the city of Baton Rouge to a brand new building in the community of Covington, not far from where the surgeon lived. He no longer had to do his arduous, daily commute, and was delighted with the change. Georgie and I arrived there for my pre-op consultation on August 22, a sunny Wednesday morning.

Everything had been discussed in detail before my visit, so I was only expecting a hearing test, followed by a conversation with the doctor.

'Your hearing is stable. In fact it's slightly better than when we last tested it in December 2011,' said Dr Gianoli. 'That's not unusual. We quite often find there's a little fluctuation in the hearing of our SCDS patients. Now, could you please summarise for me all the symptoms that you're currently experiencing.'

I hadn't anticipated being asked this, and had no prepared list, so my response was rambling.

'I've been doing my best to avoid supermarkets again; I dread going up and down those long aisles, and I live in fear of meeting someone there, as I need to get in and out of shops like that as quickly as possible. I'm constantly bumping into doors and walls – you know what I mean, misjudging everything. I feel as though I'm swaying slightly a lot of the time, no doubt some people think I'm drunk, and it does make me feel incredibly self-conscious. I don't like people walking behind me, as I always feel they are watching me wobbling around. I nearly fell down into the gap between a train and the platform the other week, when I was getting off at Edinburgh station. That gave me a bit of a shock. It's a struggle throughout the day – my brain almost aches from having to work overtime to keep me upright, or moving in a straight line.'

Dr Gianoli had been listening carefully, and he was starting to look a little unsettled.

'All the symptoms you're describing are typical of vestibular problems, but what concerns me is that they are all fairly non-specific for SCDS,' he said. 'I need to be sure there isn't another problem going on, one that could be handled with medication or some other means.'

I knew by now that dizziness and balance problems are the third most common complaint to general practitioners, after headaches and back pain, but I also knew that a scan had shown clearly that I had a remaining hole in my head. Why would Dr Gianoli be in any doubt that it was the cause of my difficulties? I had travelled thousands of miles to have this conversation, and had already made the payment for the operation scheduled for the next morning – I could sense alarm showing on my face as I looked at him.

'I just want to run two more tests, and that should hopefully give me the answers I need,' he told me. 'We'll get them done straightaway.'

The visual test with the goggles on (ENG) clearly confirmed that sound going into my right ear did indeed make me dizzy, something I had not been sure about when asked. But even more revealing was the moving platform test (CDP), which I had done a couple of times in the past, but never before found such an enormous strain. Most of the balancing on the platform, as it tipped backwards and forwards, was done with the eyes shut. The amount of concentration it required from me on this occasion was gigantic, and my neck and shoulders ached more and more as the minutes ticked by. The conclusive part of this test was the measuring of my balance before and after putting pressure in the ear. In a patient with a normal inner ear, the pressure would have had no affect, but my inner ear was stimulated by it, and notable imbalance was the result. This aspect helped confirm that my second ear was indeed symptomatic, and that the first ear had been successfully treated. My surgeon's mind was put at rest – SCDS on the right side appeared to be the source of my symptoms. Dr Gianoli subsequently told me it re-emphasised for him how important such tests were, in terms of reaching a correct diagnosis.

There was an important lesson to learn from the morning's visit, and one to which all SCDS patients and doctors treating them would be advised to pay attention. Just because a person has the anatomic findings of a hole in their superior semicircular canal, it does not automatically follow that the hole is the cause of their problems. Dr Gianoli had been witness to this fact on numerous occasions. Some with the anatomic findings had no symptoms at all. Some had a hole visible on a scan on one side, but their vestibular problem was actually on the opposite side. And in my case there were several other pathologies that could have been the cause of symptoms – BPPV, PLF or hydrops (as discussed in earlier chapters), uncompensated vestibulopathy, or even the possibility that the first ear had not been successfully treated. Dr Gianoli was, he said, 'a believer in measuring twice and cutting once.'

Arrival back at North Oaks Medical Center the next morning was at the relatively relaxed time of eight. The surgery was starting later than usual, as Dr Gianoli was attending a school ceremony for his son's transition into Senior High School. He proudly showed me a photo on his phone as I lay on my trolley, trembling in my thin hospital gown – it wasn't from fearful anticipation of the operation, rather the freezing cold of the holding area. A surgical nurse fetched a heated blanket to drape over me. I now knew the morning's order of events only too well – I would exchange some pleasantries with a few members of the operating team, identify myself, and then be gently transported to my soporific land of blissful ignorance, after the anaesthetist had located an obliging vein to pierce.

When I regained consciousness, it was in semi-darkness on an intensive care bed, and I was in the company of a nurse in his early twenties, whose offbeat look with dark beard and blue hair band added to my disorientation, pickled as I was on potent painkillers. His soft voice and reassuring manner, however, made him a perfect night watchman, and during my lucid patches we engaged in whispered conversations in the gloom, discussing among other things how his American name Travis had transmuted into Trevor, of Welsh origin, and why it had become necessary for me to make so many return visits across the Atlantic.

Several nurses had stirred my admiration during the years of medical treatment, but this individual left a lasting impression. There are times in life when, for many reasons, it becomes easier to find a connection with a stranger than to open up to those close to us. I felt privileged to have the undivided attention, for the duration of the night, of someone who radiated sincerity, and showed a deep understanding for others, despite his young age. If there was one lesson that I had learned above all else in the past decade, it was the value of honest communication in personal relationships, as well as those that developed with medical professionals. Emotions need to be expressed freely, and only bad outcomes result from communication breakdown.

It amused Trevor that, having kept my blood pressure perfectly stable throughout the night, it was my surgeon who prompted it to shoot up the scale. Leaning over me early in the morning to take a look at my head, he woke me with a start in doing so.

'Oh, I am sorry,' said Dr Gianoli. We all laughed.

'I was trying not to disturb you but instead I made you jump. How are you feeling? The surgery went very well. I didn't find anything unexpected this time, but you did have quite a large hole in there.'

The fact that Dr Gianoli had encountered nothing untoward was exactly the news I needed to hear. I felt an immediate release of tension. The discovery of quite a large hole was probably the most satisfying aspect. There could never again be any shadow of a doubt that I had had holes on both sides of my head, and never again could any doctor back home dispute that fact. Dr Gianoli had treated patients with SCDS for longer than anyone in the world, starting in January 1998, and by the time of writing his total number of SCDS surgeries had easily surpassed three hundred – there was no-one else who had done anywhere near that number. The only person who had treated the condition prior to him had been Dr Minor, and he had retired from clinical practice some time ago. Dr Gianoli had now opened up both sides of my head. He had found not one but two holes, of about the same size, in the superior semicircular canals, and he had repaired those holes. I would need time to take it in, but it was starting to dawn on me that I was coming to the end of a journey that, for years and years, had seemed as though it had no end.

Our next meeting was the following morning at 7.30 am, when Dr Gianoli greeted me with a smile in my hospital room. After a short talk, he gave me the all clear to return to the hotel to complete the remaining few days of my bed rest, where my sister would look after me. Aside from my post-op check in five days' time, Dr Gianoli knew that I had an important visit to make to my salivary gland surgeon before I flew back to London – he was going to administer at least one Botox injection. Lovely as it would have been just to see Dr Walvekar again, there was a serious purpose behind this plan, and it wasn't to provide me with an unlined, expressionless face with the age-defying properties of the drug. At the time of reading about rats and the effects of sectioning their nerves, I had also educated myself on some of the medicinal benefits of Botulinum toxin type A. Studies had clearly demonstrated its ability to significantly reduce the acinar cells which secrete saliva, and there were functional glandular changes after its application. Notwithstanding, Dr Walvekar had expressed some reservation.

'My concern is not whether Botox will work,' he had written in an email, 'but whether there is any obvious salivary gland tissue that can still be targeted, now that we've removed two of your glands. I've also got concern about a potential facial palsy from the injection.'

Nevertheless, the two surgeons and I all agreed it was worth a try, and that Dr Walvekar would be the best person for the task. I was planning to see him once my bed rest was over. Before we parted company, Dr Gianoli mentioned some precautions that were underway for an incoming storm. As I was going to be confined to bed, I didn't pay a great deal of attention to his weather forecast.

'Be good,' he said, as he opened the door to leave.

'I always am,' I replied, not for the first time but maybe the last.

In fact it wasn't just any old storm that was brewing. Storm Isaac, originating off the western coast of Africa, turned into a Category 1 hurricane, and it was heading directly our way. Before the full force of it hit Louisiana on Tuesday, August 28, a state of emergency had been declared in the region, and thousands of residents in the low-lying areas were being evacuated. It was happening a mere seven years after the severe devastation caused by hurricane Katrina (Category 5), and Louisiana once more suffered very badly, as the effects proved to be more extreme in that state than anywhere else in the storm's path.

From the safety of our hotel suite, Georgie and I watched the rain lashing down, and heard the winds buffeting the building and everything else in their way. We were thankful that the hotel had its own generator, and all our needs could be met without leaving the premises. We monitored the unfolding of events hour by hour on our large television screen, and were filled with sympathy for so many local residents who were being put through tremendous hardship. I knew that Dr Walvekar would be experiencing problems, as the areas north and south of New Orleans, the city in which he lived, were flooded. Having originally had contact with him by text, it was no longer possible to reach him. The strong gales caused a widespread power outage, and by Wednesday the concern for Georgie and I certainly wasn't whether Botox could be administered, but whether we would be able to fly home as scheduled on Friday, and how Dr Gianoli was going to undertake my post-op assessment without any power to work equipment in his clinic.

I didn't need any convincing that Dr Gianoli was a dedicated doctor, and when he contacted me to say that he and his wife were kayaking their way out of the driveway from their house, so that he could attend my post-op appointment as planned, it seemed to be the mark of a man prepared to go above and beyond the call of duty. At least it had now stopped raining. The meeting was to be at a different location where some power was available, and his wife was still in her shorts and rubber waterproof boots when she greeted Georgie and me on arrival. When I first came out of hospital I had been extremely unsteady, and I still had to be very careful about moving my head too quickly, or tipping it up or down. I wasn't experiencing any full-blown vertigo episodes, but there were distinct indications that such an attack wasn't very far away – the sensation of the stomach falling away, as I staved off the dizziness, was happening fairly frequently, particularly if I lay my head in a flat position. I needed a seat to recover my composure within minutes of entering the building, as I felt as though I might be about to faint.

'I understand,' Dr Gianoli said. 'That is a direct result of the resurfacing that I have done over the superior canal. It will gradually settle down, give it a little time. When you do the period of bed rest, lying for five days propped up at an angle of forty-five degrees, it is of course preventing some of these occurrences. Now your body has to adjust to being up and about.'

The surgeon carefully pulled out the first inner layer of packing from my ear, and then removed the staples over my stitches. Everything was healing well, and there was really very little pain. I could feel with my finger the neat scar running round behind my ear, with just a short curve heading upwards under my hair. Many of the external noises invading my head I recognised from previous surgeries – additional layers of sound, ranging from squeaks and Mickey Mouse chatterings, to faint pulsations. Others, including the clicking shut of a suitcase as Georgie prepared for our departure in the hotel room, took a while to identify. My eyes scanned the surroundings, searching for the source of any alien noises.

I was declared fit to fly home. We hugged my surgeon good-bye and thanked him and his wife for all the effort they had expended to enable us to catch the flight. We could not have predicted that, having weathered the hurricane and slowly driven through the drenched region to get back to Baton Rouge airport on time, our plane would sit on the runway owing to a technical fault, and cause us to miss the connecting flight at Atlanta.

We got to know Atlanta's brand new Maynard H. Jackson international terminal thoroughly, as there was no flight to London we could be put on until the following day. It comprised a very modern-looking series of open spaces, with huge, glass expanses and bright white discs hanging in clusters from the ceiling. It seemed a fairly calm atmosphere to wander around, and it wasn't until I stepped inside an elevator and discovered blissful quiet in the soundproof box, that the extent of airport noise bombardment became evident to me. It was as though I had escaped from the confines of a squirling dishwasher come discotheque, with music emanating from the shops and cafés, announcements spiralling down from the tannoy system, and the shrill vocalizations of passengers on the move bouncing around the space. I didn't yet have total confidence to test out my new level of stability, but I was already aware that it had become easier for me to look up at the flight departure screens, and shift my gaze from side to side.

A recent study of ballet dancers' brains has confirmed the brain's amazing ability to adapt. The technique they employ of 'spotting' – rapidly and repeatedly focusing on two points in front of, and behind, them – certainly seems to help prevent them falling over after spinning in circles, but there is more going on. When sensation perception and eye reflexes were measured, dancers were shown to be much more resistant than non-dancers, and MRI scans revealed that the dancers had smaller areas of white matter in the cerebellum. The grey matter is the part of the brain that calculates, and the white matter is the part that makes connections, and is involved in processing signals from the ear. The more experienced the dancer, the smaller that area was, so the flow of signals was being reduced. 'More white matter means you're more likely to be dizzy – in dancers we didn't see it,' said the neurologist Dr Barry Seemungal, at Imperial College in London. 'The brain is the organ that controls balance, and crucially, it's able to adapt.' Luckily, for the purpose of the study, one of the dancers developed chronic dizziness, and further testing revealed that her perception response had become stronger.

Professor Clayton, at the dance company Rambert, explained one of the tricks dancers employ, to allow their bodies to move expressively without losing control: 'When you get that sense of spinning, you use your core muscles to pull up; you're disengaging with that feeling of fluidity, and creating a stabilising energy.'

After damage to the vestibular system, people can feel better, and function can return, by means of compensation – the dynamic process of the central nervous system responding and re-wiring after trauma. Central vestibular compensation occurs because the brain learns to use other faculties, such as vision and other body senses, to make up for a deficient balance system. This process takes place over time, but I could help speed up my recovery by dusting off the list of exercises that I had put into practice after my first revision surgery in 2009, and promoting compensation. My ballet career may have ended before it even got off the ground, but I did have a brain that could learn new tricks, and was able to adapt.

And most importantly, I no longer had a pair of menacing holes that had made its daily job so labour-intensive and exhausting.

23

RISING STRONG

'You have to be like Sherlock Holmes. You have to put the pieces together, find all the clues,' said Dr John Rutka in a recent interview. The head of neurotology, at the University Health Network in Toronto, identified one of his rewards at the end of the detection process as being able to tell his patients: 'You're not crazy, you're not psychotic, you're not nuts. Forget what other doctors have told you.'

If only there were more Dr Rutkas. It has been estimated that in the United States alone there are currently approximately fifteen million people suffering from the misery of chronic vestibular problems, and there are around 350 different medically recognised causes of vertigo, and other balance conditions, that could apply. It remains unknown how many of those fifteen million may be afflicted with SCDS, but in 2011 Dr Minor expressed the view that the syndrome wasn't as rare as originally thought: 'We don't have enough data to give an actual number, but you can just see from the papers, and the cases being reported, that it may not be all that rare.' Dr Gianoli's opinion, in 2016, is that its incidence among those who have chronic dizziness is probably in excess of fifteen percent. He also points out that there are a number of others, with dehiscences of other parts of the inner ear, who have symptoms that are identical to those of SCDS.

Potential sufferers, who are likely to find themselves bandying around the words dizzy and dizziness, would be wise to heed the warning of author P.J. Haybach, and take note that those terms don't have a precise meaning in the healthcare world: 'Don't make the mistake of assuming people understand what you're talking about; there's a good chance they don't but are just nodding their heads because they were taught to be reassuring.' Dizziness incorporates a long list of symptoms – 'lightheadedness, faintness, movement illusions, feelings of non-reality, floating, swimming or rocking sensations, spinning, nausea and queasiness, to name but a few.' I certainly learned the hard way how important it was to be as specific as possible when describing what was happening to me.

Doctors with a lack of ENT expertise, who see patients complaining of dizziness, tend to conclude that those past the age of forty may be suffering from a heart attack or stroke, and those under forty from low blood pressure. 'But there is nothing the heart can do that will make you feel you are spinning,' clarifies Dr Gianoli. Heart rate can be affected by the vestibular system though, as the vestibulosympathetic reflex runs directly between it and the sympathetic division of the autonomic nervous system. This reflex can affect heart rate and blood pressure (usually increasing, but sometimes decreasing them), trigger all the usual fight or flight responses, and most notably cause the release of adrenaline. When a sufficient quantity of it is released, significant anxiety and even panic attacks will follow.

The relationship between anxiety and SCDS revolves in a vicious circle. Dizziness made me feel anxious, anxiety made me feel dizzy, and the more the two collided, the more anxious I became. Social situations were particularly treacherous, and those that involved holding a glass became the ones I feared most of all. My hand would start to tremble and shake, threatening to spill the drink, my limbs would turn to jelly, and my mind was so wrapped up in the unwanted physical sensations taking place that I often found it almost impossible to engage in relaxed social interactions. Many patients with inner ear problems, me included, also seem to have more issues with nausea than other people – something Dr Gianoli was able to confirm based on his experience, although there are no studies examining this. He expounded his view: 'If you are on the borderline of getting nauseated all the time, any little bit of anything else that can make you nauseated will tip you over the edge.'

For years I had no explanation for the difficulties that I was keeping secret, so it was perhaps hardly surprising that at times I questioned my mental state. I didn't have a Dr Rutka at hand to assure me I wasn't nuts. The vestibulospinal reflex extends from the inner ear to all the postural muscles, and limb tremors and weakness can occur with abnormal vestibular stimulation, even though they have not been well reported in the literature. As a physiotherapist put it, 'it is a common symptom of anxiety to have muscle twitching and spasming in various parts of the body, and of course with SCDS anxiety is amped to the max.'

No-one doubts that there is a psychological component at work, and scientists are beginning to get to grips with the very basic wiring in the brain that links dizziness to panic. Professor Carey Balaban, a neurobiologist at the University of Pittsburgh, has been undertaking studies on rats and monkeys, and his team has pinpointed direct connections between the cluster of neurons in the brain stem that mediate arousal, fear and anger (locus coeruleus), and the vestibular nuclei which process signals from the inner ear. A junction along the route is the parabrachial nucleus, and from there the nerve fibres can communicate with the neural pathways that mediate anxiety. There is a clear two-way linkage between balance and anxiety, and this underlying network in the brain would explain why I became a prisoner of my own thought processes, trapped in a recurring and self-destructive pattern of worry about when the next dizzy or panic attack would strike. 'If you don't trust your balance system, anxiety is a natural protective process,' explains Professor Balaban.

Vestibular dysfunction may bring about even more profound effects, ones that could be classified as personality changes. Studies have been published which demonstrate depersonalisation and derealisation symptoms in dizzy patients, pointing to the fact that the vestibular system plays a part in various aspects of higher consciousness – cognition, emotion and even the sense of self are involved. Research indicates that the temporoparietal junction (TPJ) in the brain, an area where two lobes meet, may prove to be the site where vestibular information is integrated with other sensory input. Future neurobiological studies will hopefully reveal how and why the depersonalisation and derealisation symptoms are created.

More Dr Rutkas, more Professor Balabans, more Dr Gianolis, and more time to evaluate and listen to dizzy patients – they are all urgently required. The physicians I encountered were at times brusque, one or two even hostile and they quite frequently didn't believe anything was wrong enough to pursue. In their eyes I seemed to be a relatively fit and high-functioning person, but as far as I saw it, my life was slowly disintegrating. Why was it so difficult for doctor and patient to communicate with each other? Insufficient time within an inconsistent system was a major problem, and I often felt I was dealing with emotionally deficient people, who were dismissive and sometimes stressed, taking out their frustrations on their patients. I understand why many doctors dislike people looking to google for answers, for the obvious reasons that they commonly obtain misinformation, and are ill-equipped to evaluate their sources for reliability, but if it hadn't been for the internet I would never have made any progress with my diagnosis, or found a route for recovery after a failed operation. My patient journey was much harder than it should have been, and it was my refusal to give up and my determination not to let my illness take over my life that saw me through, and ensured

I found my American heroes. For that's what they were to me, heroes.

It could be argued that the British medical system failed me, but regrettably the legal process didn't redress the balance. Early in March 2013, a document was forwarded to me by my lawyer, in which the expert witness for the potential clinical negligence claim laid forth his conclusions in a detailed report. We had been waiting many months for this to happen, and just as many hours had been spent chasing up the report. I didn't delay in voicing my dissatisfaction in a written reply to the lawyer, and I knew he would be as frustrated as I was about the outcome.

'I feel disheartened and angry. Angry with our expert for letting twenty months go by since I saw him in London, before deciding that he cannot be "entirely supportive". He claims to have prepared a balanced report "without bias introduced through my knowledge of the surgeon in question, and indeed his excellent reputation", but he hasn't really done that. He is clearly influenced by knowing him, and by his reputation, and the report could only be balanced if he had reviewed all the necessary accompanying evidence, which he doesn't appear to have done – I'm referring in particular to the crucial CT scan which, since writing the report, he has agreed confirms I have bilateral SCDS. Mr Ingram may have an excellent reputation, I have never doubted that, but anyone can make mistakes, in particular when they are doing a procedure for the first time. I feel hugely frustrated and disappointed that our expert witness seems to think it is acceptable for a doctor to: a) incompletely diagnose a patient; b) discharge them when the symptoms have clearly not resolved; c) ignore a series of test results; d) fail to intervene *of his own accord* when the patient is obviously still suffering, and has continually told the doctor that; e) choose not to communicate with another SCDS specialist (Dr Gianoli) with far more experience, when the opportunity arose; f) continue to claim that it was better to do nothing, and let the patient suffer. I simply don't understand how he can believe that the evidence presented by my surgeon is satisfactory, when there were so many gaps, and so many unanswered questions, in my correspondence with the NHS Trust.'

By informing us that he couldn't be entirely supportive, the expert witness was spelling out that he wasn't prepared to stand up in a court of law to defend my claim, despite the fact that he had outlined in his report the way in which he would have handled my treatment differently, and why he would have re-operated on me. He was more than happy to charge me a substantial fee for providing his report, but unless he was equally happy to make his views public, the claim could not advance to the next stage, and my mother would have no hope of ever again seeing the many thousands of pounds she had invested in my medical treatment abroad. There is no justice in this world, some would say, and I now had quite a few reasons to agree. It was with very mixed feelings that I heard the news some months later that my original surgeon had undertaken not one, but two, revision surgeries on one of his SCDS patients further down the line. A sign, perhaps, that something had been learned from the debacle in my case?

Was the repair of my right-sided hole in the head successful? An unequivocal yes was the answer. Did I wish that Dr Gianoli had been my physician from the very beginning of the story? An unequivocal yes again. But I grew, I changed, and 'rising strong is how we cultivate wholeheartedness in our lives; it's the process that teaches us the most about who we are', says social scientist Brené Brown. 'The process of regaining our emotional footing in the midst of struggle is where our courage is tested, and our values are forged.' Like Brené Brown, I recognised the importance of the qualities of 'toughness, doggedness and perseverance', and I knew I wouldn't return to being the person I was when I started down the long SCDS path – one who knew little about how to advocate for herself. I had learned to let go of the need to always please people and seek approval, and I trusted my instinct.

I also considered myself an optimist, and according to the science journalist Jo Marchant that may have stood me in good stead. Realism can be bad for your health, optimists recover better. Taking a rosy view of the future is helpful, but so is having a rosy view of yourself, as high 'self-enhancers' have lower cardiovascular responses to stress, and lower baseline cortisol levels. Furthermore, a study released from North Carolina State University, in November 2015, suggests that those who have survived a major stress event, such as divorce (and, one would assume, brain surgery), are better able to cope with the ups and downs of day-to-day stress, as they show more resilience and more stability in their responses. My future was clearly going to be a breeze. I had emerged with a new appreciation of life and a gradual acceptance of the fluid symptoms from the nerve reaction, even though the pain and discomfort would have to be managed day in and day out, without fail. 'Why me?' was a question I eventually stopped asking my surgeon.

'In your situation, I'll bet it's probably a combination of trauma or pressure, along with some pre-existing susceptibility,' explained Dr Gianoli. 'I know that sounds vague, but it's actually a common scenario in medicine. Why do we see some people who get hearing loss from noise exposure, while others exposed to the same amount don't get any hearing loss at all? Pre-existing susceptibility.'

Nevertheless, I didn't immediately abandon all attempts at eliminating the fluid build-up, once I had returned home from Louisiana in August 2012. With customary thoughtfulness, Dr Walvekar wrote to apologise for not being able to administer any Botox injections, and explained that the very day their power resumed on September 2, his family had received a call from India that a family member was critically ill. Within hours they departed for India, and were away for several weeks. Unfortunately his relation did not recover. Early in 2013, with Dr Walvekar's knowledge, I made contact with Dr Kubba, a refreshingly obliging doctor in Scotland, who needed little persuading to take charge of the Botox plan. Two injections were administered inside my mouth, one into the remaining sub-lingual gland under my tongue, and one inside my cheek into the duct that had led into the parotid gland, now long gone. Dr Walvekar's earlier reservations unfortunately proved well founded, but I had been excited when I first wrote to tell Dr Gianoli my news.

'I know the Botox is doing something, but I'd really better not say much more than that at this point, other than to add that I'm having quite a lot of trouble swallowing today. I think I sound as though I have a speech impediment, and I know my tongue can't reach parts of my mouth that it usually can. Of course I know these are all potential side effects of Botox, and they should wear off.'

But in fact the side effects took weeks and weeks to wear off, and they completely cancelled out any benefits.

'I sound like a drunken, deaf person who has had dental treatment, and it's very tiring,' I told my sister, to whom I had given the nickname Nursie. How could I ever repay her for everything she'd done to help me? 'Botox itself seems to have made me feel drained of energy, but all the effort with eating and talking is extremely tiring as well.'

Two operations followed – in Scotland, not Louisiana. One was a straightforward procedure to tie up the parotid duct, and the other a hideously painful removal of the sublingual gland. I then had no more major salivary glands on the troubled side of my face, so there was nothing left to remove. Just in case I needed any further convincing that Devil's Breath wasn't my solution either, new research published in April 2016 confirmed the potential adverse effects of scopolamine, and all other drugs falling into the anticholinergic category. The conclusions of the study were that such medications could definitely affect memory and shrink the brain, and the more you took the worse the impact.

The final attempt to conquer the nerve problem involved the insertion of a ventilation tube of a slightly enlarged variety, in the hope it would make my symptoms more manageable by assisting the fluid to drain away naturally inside my head, and equalising the pressure inside my middle ear.

I arrived for the pre-op assessment. I was back inside the gloomy 1960s, box-like building in Edinburgh, where five years earlier I had visited the kindly Dr Kerr (doctor no.5), and the not so kindly Dr Miller (doctor no.6). I sat in the large waiting area, devoid as it had always been of any brightening decorative touches, and my thoughts turned to the many events that had drawn me to the clinic, and then flung me very much further afield. The memories were making me feel uncomfortable, and I was relieved to see a smiling face, when Nurse Anne strode through one of the doors to collect me. We sat down on the hard chairs in her tiny office, where there was just enough space for us and a small desk, on which she had stacked several neat piles of green folders. She took a blood pressure monitor out of the drawer, and then wrapped the cuff around my outstretched arm.

'I've been reading through your notes, Philippa,' she said. 'You've certainly been through the mill, haven't you? How many surgeries have you had altogether?'

I smiled at her. 'I've almost lost count now – including the one coming up, ten I think.'

She removed the cuff and made a note of the reading.

'Your blood pressure is perfect, that's excellent,' she said. 'So tell me, Superior Semicircular Canal Dehiscence Syndrome. I don't think I've ever come across this before, can you explain what it is?'

It wasn't the first time I'd had such a question posed to me by an ENT professional, and I was sure it wouldn't be the last. I was always dismayed to find they hadn't heard of the condition, and what immediately sprung to mind were all the poor patients who desperately needed them to get better informed. I launched into a quick summary of the symptoms, and the trouble I'd had getting a diagnosis, and then wrote down for Anne a link to an online article I'd written the previous year.

'That's very helpful,' she said. 'I'll look it up as soon as I get home, and read all about it.'

I could see she meant it. She fixed me with her gaze, her twinkly blue eyes suddenly full of concern.

'You don't know what you don't know,' she said.

BOOKS REFERRED TO

Cousins, Norman. *Anatomy of an Illness as Perceived by the Patient*. NY: W.W. Norton & Co. 1979

Didion, Joan. *The Year of Magical Thinking*. London: Harper Perennial 2006

Haybach, P.J. *Inner Ear Balance and Dizziness Disorders*. BookSurge, LLC 2005

Klitzman, Robert. *When Doctors Become Patients*. Oxford University Press 2008

McCredie, Scott. *Balance*. NY: Little, Brown and Company 2007

Popper, Karl. *The Open Society and Its Enemies*. London: Routledge 1966

Sanders, Lisa. *Every Patient Tells a Story*. NY: Broadway Books 2009

Selye, Hans. *The Stress of Life*. NY: The McGraw-Hill Companies, Inc. 1978

Sollier, Pierre. *Listening for Wellness*. Walnut Creek, CA: The Mozart Center Press 2005

ACKNOWLEDGEMENTS

This book would not have come into being, were it not for Dr Gianoli. Restoring my health (an enormous achievement in itself), generously sharing his knowledge and experience, encouraging me to proceed with the writing, as well as making time to read the manuscript and clarify some of the medical content – my gratitude to this exceptional man knows no bounds. It was also a pleasure to have the contribution of Dr James Soileau, his partner at The Ear and Balance Institute. Dr Soileau read the manuscript too, and showed the same level of encouragement and interest.

Warmest thanks go to my other readers, David, Harriet and Mairi – for devoting their time, and for the constructive comments they passed on. Out of the long list of those who offered me support over the years, Arna, Charlie, Janice and Mitchell, all with direct experience of SCDS, deserve a special mention. Their personal stories also helped inspire me to write the book. As well as being an outstanding friend, Jan gave me the helping eye of an artist, to steer me through to my book cover choices. Then Eric and Janet, my carefully selected photographer and designer, brought the ideas to life.

Thank you all.

35561097R00145

Made in the USA
San Bernardino, CA
28 June 2016